Herefordshire

A CAMRA Guide to the County's

C000214372

CONTENTS

Researched by members of the Herefordshire Branch of the Campaign for Real Ale.

Front Cover Illustrations		
New Inn, Pembridge	Sun Inn, Leintwardine	Wine Vaults, Kington
Oak, Staplow	Cross Keys, Withington	Bell Inn, Leominster
Black Swan, Hereford	Cottage of Content, Carey	

Printed on recycled paper by

REPRODUX PRINTERS LTD., Hereford, (01432) 269341

ISBN 10: 1-85249-237-6
>ISBN 13: 978-1-85249-237-3

How to use the Herefordshire Pub Guide

Town or village ▶ **TITLEY JUNCTION**   **A2**   ◀ County map grid reference

Pub name ▶ **Ghost Train**

Address ▶ **Station Road, HR3 5MT**   2 miles S of B4318   ◀ Directions

OS map ref ▶ OS345678

(01981) 170635   ◀ Telephone number

Website ▶ www.ghosttrainpub.co.uk

12-2.30 (not Mon), 7-11; 12-midnight Fri, Sat; 12-10.30 Sun   ◀ Opening times

Beers & ciders ▶ **Beer Engine Piston Bitter; Cottage Golden Arrow; Dunn Plowman Railway Porter; guest beers (2): Black Rat Cider**

Dispense ▶ **[G]**

Situated near the site of the long closed station, this ◀ Description of pub
pub still clings to its memories of the heyday of the
railways, with its spartan public and cosy lounge bars
liberally adorned with old photographs and memorabilia. The BR style sandwiches are guaranteed three
days old, whilst the steak & kidney pies, the only 'hot'
food on offer, are kept warm in a cabinet on the bar
(not Sun eves). The landlord keeps time with his cher-
ished guard's pocket watch. Anoraks are welcome.

Facilities ▶ 🔥 ❀ 🛏 ◖◗ ♿ ⛺ 🚌 ♣ P

KEY TO SYMBOLS

🔥 **Real fire:** a fire fuelled by coal, smoke-less fuel or logs

Q **Quiet pub:** free from piped music, juke-boxes, electronic games and TVs (at least one room)

🐾 **Family room:** where the licensee guar-antees that families are warmly (and le-gally) welcome in their own separate room, or distinctly separate area.

❀ **Outdoor drinking area:** this may vary from a garden to benches on a pave-ment, or even a village green

🛏 **Accommodation:** rooms to let (no as-sessment of quality or price is made)

◖ **Lunchtime meals:** not snacks but sub-stantial fare (including one hot dish) and in the pub itself, not in a separate restau-rant

◗ **Evening meals:** as for lunchtime meals; separate restaurants are often mentioned in the pub description

🍺 **Public bar:** a traditional public bar

♿ **Wheelchair access:** easy access to the pub and WCs (where fully equipped WC is available this is stated in the text)

⛺ **Camping:** camping facilities for tents at the pub or within one mile; sometimes caravans are also welcomed

⇌ **Near railway station:** within 15 mins walk

🚌 **Bus service:** Bus service enabling return trip from a town at least five days per week

♣ **Traditional pub games played**

🍺 **Real draught cider:** (not keg cider) - at least one available

P **Pub has its own car park**

⚡ **No-smoking room or area:** a specially designated smoke-free zone, available to drinkers and not just diners.

▽ **Oversized lined pint glasses:** used for some or all beers

About this Guide

Scope: All pubs in the county of Herefordshire, with emphasis on those serving real ale, plus any other outlets for draught real ale or cider provided they are open to the public without admission charge at all reasonable hours.

There are a number of pubs in the HR postcode area, addressed as Herefordshire, particularly in Hay-on-Wye, that are not in the County and are therefore not included. Conversely, some pubs in the SY and WR areas lie within the county and are included.

Ordnance Survey reference (OS): given for pubs not in towns or villages with street names, and not on A or B roads. The County of Herefordshire falls entirely within National Grid square SO.

Hours: starts with Monday then lists other days if they are different; "am" only used for hours after midnight, and "pm" for sessions starting at 8pm or later. Therefore, for example, "10-11" or "9-midnight" mean all day opening.

Dispense of beer or cider is by handpump unless otherwise noted (see p 12):
  [G] by gravity straight from the cask
  [P] by electric pump

Food: This guide does not attempt to judge the food in a pub, but simply aims to give an impression of the type of meals on offer. It is always advisable to telephone to verify the availability of food before setting out, particularly on Sunday evenings.

Disabled access: As CAMRA members are not normally qualified to assess facilities for disabled customers, this guide uses the wheelchair symbol to indicate pubs which are believed to be *reasonably accessible* to wheelchairs and where staff can be expected to be helpful. Where a fully equipped toilet is available this is indicated in the text. The number of fully equipped pubs remains low, in spite of the Disability Discrimination Act of 2004, which so far has only impacted on pubs making significant structural alterations.

Beer Quality: This guide does not comment directly on the quality of the real ales on offer in the pubs. To find the pubs regarded by Herefordshire Branch as offering consistently good quality, consult the Good Beer Guide published annually by CAMRA

Acknowledgements
Production team: Paul Grenfell, Mark Haslam, Alan Simpson

Mapping/photography: Paul Grenfell   Articles: Mark Haslam, Alan Simpson

Pub Survey Team: Vernon Amor, Alison Clarke, Des Clarke, Mick Collins, Jon Cooke, Geoff Cooper, Janet Crowther, Simon Crowther, Peter Goody, Paul Grenfell, Susan Grenfell, Mark Haslam, Tony Hobbs, Paul Lelievre, Chris Lewandowski, David Masters, Steve Mott, Dave Powell, Richard Putley, Malcolm Rochefort, Alan Simpson, Anthony Smith, Karen Williams

We also wish to thank our Advertisers whose generous support has helped to bring this independent guide to you. Although inclusion in this guide is not an endorsement of their goods and services, we hope you will support them by sampling their products.

WELCOME TO *HEREFORDSHIRE PUBS*

Herefordshire Pubs is the only comprehensive guide to the pubs of Herefordshire: covering *all* the pubs across the county. This is the second edition of this book in this format, following two earlier guides in the 1980s. We never imagined back in August, 2003, when the first edition was published, how successful it would be. It immediately shot to the top of the local book charts - and remained a best seller until it sold out completely only three months later! We were delighted to find that our enthusiasm for the great pubs of Herefordshire was shared by so many people. We are hopeful that this fully-updated and revamped second edition will be just as successful.

Unlike some other so-called pub guides, we do not take any payment from any of the pubs listed: we pride ourselves on the independence and objectivity of this publication. We firmly believe that you would rather read our viewpoint as fellow pub-goers, than pay to read the advertising spin of various publicans - conveniently disguised as a 'pub guide'. All the work in compiling this guide is done entirely by unpaid CAMRA volunteers. Local CAMRA members have been working feverishly over the past six months to thoroughly survey every single pub in the county, and rest-assured any surplus funds that we might make in sales will be re-invested in CAMRA campaigns and projects (locally and nationally) that champion the cause of the pub consumer.

This guide has pubs for all tastes and all occasions. There are city bars, town pubs as well as country pubs and inns. Whether you are seeking out good food, good beer, a rare farmhouse cider, or perhaps just a pub that is ideal for families - we've got the lot. With all the county's 284 pubs and bars listed, there are enough pubs to keep you going at the rate of one-a-day for the best part of a working year. In particular, we hope you'll take the opportunity get out to some of the county's many excellent village inns. Herefordshire is a uniquely unspoiled English county, with country pubs waiting to be discovered just around the corner. Whether your pub odyssey takes you to a remote ex-drovers' inn high in the hills on the Welsh border; a more sedate country pub amongst wooded lanes, a riverside pub unchanged for centuries, or a pub located high on the Malvern Hills - you'll find the lot in here, and everything in between too. Each pub's details are fully listed with their facilities and opening hours, along with the real beers and cider they sell. All the pubs in Hereford city and the other towns come with easy-to-understand maps to help you plan that special pub crawl.

We've added a few interesting articles for you to enjoy on those trips down the pub: information on public transport to help you get there in the first place, and an item on tourism for ideas of what to do before doors open. Further articles cover a number of issues that affect the pub-user and the pub industry. In particular, this publication makes no apology for banging on about the many issues threatening our rural pubs. They've been having a tough time for quite a few years now. It is our view that there is a chink of light, and that people are increasingly starting to re-discover our rural pub heritage, but we can't relax as country and village pubs continue to close. We hope you will use this guide to get out and explore those pubs, as they deserve your custom.

We would like to hear from you. What do you think of the guide? How can we improve it? Have we missed anything? Certainly, we'd be very grateful if you could let us know of any changes (hours, beers, facilities etc.) when you visit a pub. You can do this by going online at www.herefordcamra.org.uk or by filling out the slip towards the back of this book and posting it to us at the address provided. Finally, you can also log-on to get regular *Herefordshire Pubs* updates - allowing you to keep your guide as up-to-date as possible.

CAMRA has over 80,000 members nationwide organised into nearly 200 local branches across the UK. The Herefordshire Branch of CAMRA is one such branch. As well as producing this guide, Herefordshire CAMRA also organise *Beer on the Wye* - the annual Hereford Beer & Cider Festival - held each summer on the banks of the Wye at the Hereford Rowing Club. We produce a regular local newsletter, *Hereford Hopvine,* and have a website at www.herefordcamra.org.uk. As well as actively campaigning on pub-consumers' rights at national and local level, we also support the efforts of local brewers, cider makers and our more enlightened publicans. Why not get involved? It isn't just about campaigning - we also have a regular and lively social programme: visiting pubs, breweries and organising many fun events. More information and CAMRA membership details can be found on page 86. You never know, you might even end up working on the next edition of this guide!

This guide has taken a lot of time, effort and money to produce. We do it because we believe in the great pubs of Herefordshire. Why not get out there and find out what it is that makes this idyllic county and its pubs so special? If you don't, then those pubs might not be there for you tomorrow.

TRENDS – A lot has happened since the last edition of *this guide*, and there's more to come....

TIME PLEASE!

On the 24th November, 2005 time was called - and the last vestiges of our ridiculous licensing laws were consigned to the drip tray of history when the Licensing Act 2003 came into force. Pubs, bars are licensed cafes were at last allowed to open when they (and their customers) wanted, subject to proper public consultation and local authority scrutiny. The previous arcane laws were imposed by the Lloyd George Government during World War I to prevent drunkenness amongst munitions workers. Fifty, sixty, and even seventy years later, those same ludicrous laws prevented anyone from buying a drink after 3.00pm in the afternoon, and created the chaos on our streets the length and breadth of the land as pubs and bars turfed out their frustrated customers en masse at 11.00pm. We ask: when was the last time you bumped into a munitions worker in a drunken stupor down at your local?

By the turn of the millennium it had (at last) suddenly occurred to those in power, that perhaps after 80 years, that those 'emergency laws' were no longer fit for purpose in an economy that relies so significantly on tourism and the hospitality trade. Foreign tourism brings in £91.8 billion per annum to the UK economy (2002-3 data) - is it really wise to continue to deny readily-spending tourists the opportunity of a drink in a bar, pub or café just because it is 4.30pm in the afternoon, or after the hour of 11.00pm? Today we have the outrageous situation prevailing were pubs, hotels and cafes open when they and their customers want them to. Disgusting! The pubs of England and Wales have at last pulled into line with Continental Europe....and, for that matter, the House of Commons Bar!

For all the right reasons, CAMRA has always championed the cause of sensible licensing hours, recognising the many benefits it would bring. It is our belief that the vast majority of pubgoers are actually quite capable of acting like sensible adults when on licensed premises. However, the more hysterical elements of the great British press found such a notion a total anathema. Before the insane laws were repealed, certain newspapers (the usual suspects) conjured up visions of rivers of vomit and riots on our streets in a drink-fuelled holocaust created by the new civilised licensing laws. They also ranted on ad nauseam about the perils of 24-hour opening. So what actually happened? You'll not be surprised to learn that it has been a near universal success, thus the reason the very same newspapers have conspicuously failed to cover the story since the laws changed. Drink-related crime down 35% doesn't sell newspapers, perhaps? And as for all the pubs being open 24 hours, seven days a week.....have a look in this guide and count up the number of pubs that open for 24 hours continuously. Clue: it's a round number! Pubgoers, publicans and the law enforcement agencies are now in general agreement that it was the right move, and not before time.

FUMING AT THE BAR

During the currency of this guide another earth-shattering change will affect the pubs and bars of Herefordshire. In the summer of 2007 legislation will come into force that will outlaw smoking in the bars of England and Wales. Ever since Sir Walter Raleigh docked in Plymouth and hot-footed it to Queen Bess with the first packet of woodbines, smoking has been a part of our pub culture. Of course, over time attitudes change, and we now know a lot more about the risks of smoking, and passive smoking in public places. However, it is still going to come as quite a shock to many pub-goers. The industry was very uneasy about the proposal, and views within CAMRA have been quite divided too. CAMRA's ultimate preferred option would have been to provide a separate smoking room: in affect a re-creation of the old Smoke Rooms, once so popular before many pubs were opened out. All this is now speculation about past events – as our pubs will soon be smoke free for the first time ever. So what will this mean?

Interestingly, we have some good examples that might point the way to what is likely to happen. Ireland switched over to a complete smoking ban in May, 2004. Who would have thought that Ireland, with its smoking and drinking culture and ultra-traditional pubs would have led the way? And then to add to the incredulity, Scotland - land of the deep-fried Mars Bar and Scotch Pie - followed suit in January, 2006: leaving England and Wales looking very much the laggards. Many other places, including New York City, had also taken the plunge and banned smoking in public places even earlier. The analysis of what has happened to the pub trade has been very mixed. Certainly trade was, at least initially, negatively affected in Ireland, however, our ever-resourceful publicans and bar-owners have a knack of keeping all their customers happy, including their smokers. In Ireland it is now not uncommon to see structures akin to cycle sheds erected against pubs, intended for the use of smokers - perhaps bringing back schoolday memories of the furtive fag behind the bike shed? In Scotland, smokers are still using the pub en masse, and overall, it

would appear that those who smoke are acting responsibly within the law, and still managing to enjoy a visit to their local. However, it will be interesting to see if the unidentified masses who say they never went in pubs because of the 'horrid cigarette smoke' make their first return visit. Do these people really exist? That may be the acid test!

Whatever we do or say, no-smoking pubs are here to stay. Experience from Ireland suggests over time the majority of smokers will come to appreciate the positive impact on the pub's environment, however, it would be a shame to see pubs close for the sake of losing a few regular smoking customers. We will all be watching events very carefully.

TAXING TIMES

Small brewers were handed a major tax break by the Chancellor of the Exchequer in 2002. Brewers producing less than sixty thousand hectolitres of beer per annum saw their duty payments reduced. Consequently, in just under three years another 120 small breweries opened for business across the UK - making a total in excess of 570. And what is more, fewer smaller brewers are closing down - the numbers keep rising, and they are increasingly successful. As well as creating more growth in small breweries, this tax break has also given them the opportunity to invest in more and better equipment. In Herefordshire alone we can report the emergence of two new small breweries since the last edition of this guide, and Stoke Lacy-based Wye Valley Brewery has continued to go from strength to strength. It's all very good news for the pubgoer who enjoys good beer.

On the flip-side, the major brewing concerns seem less interested then ever in producing real beer. They appear to have largely abandoned quality real beer in favour of global here-today-gone-tomorrow brands of near-beers and ersatz lagers - products that seem to need endless amounts of advertising spend to keep people drinking them. The multi-nationals seem to be singularly obsessed by the 'coolness' of their latest TV advertising campaign, such that they seem to forget to put traditional quality ingredients into their products. The increasing army of small brewers are now rapidly filling the vacuum left by the multi-national brewing concerns, and as the market share for small brewers grows year on year, this suggests that the best people to brew beer are brewers after all - and not accountants or marketing luvvies!

This tax initiative has been so successful in producing a more level playing field between the larger mega-brewers and small local brewers, that there are now malign forces at work trying to persuade the Exchequer to scrap this scheme. However, CAMRA has worked hard to successfully lobby on this important concession, and we will continue to lobby Government to ensure that it stays. Today, people are becoming increasingly aware of local producers and the quality of their products. Local brewers brew beers to suit distinct local tastes - tastes that often go back centuries. Beers that might be popular in Northern England or Scotland aren't necessarily to the liking the of those that live in, say, the Midlands or the South. If they could have their way the multi-nationals would have us drinking one uniform brand (shouldn't that be bland?), but the local brewers have other ideas, and are proving increasingly that many people will not be bullied into drinking something they don't like.

There is a full list of all brewers based in Herefordshire, along with the beers they brew on page 77 of the guide. We hope you will take the opportunity to try them for yourself. Go on, give your taste buds a treat, and taste the history of Herefordshire!

FESTIVAL TIME!

CAMRA's not just about talking about beer and cider – campaigning for real beer and cider means drinking the stuff! As an active organisation we pride ourselves on professionally organising over 170 beer and cider festivals across the UK each year. These are our the shop window for good beer and cider. Beer festivals provide a superb opportunity to share with the you, the typical pub-goer, the many excellent beers, ciders and perries that those pesky accountants and marketeers at the Mega-brew Corporation plc would rather you didn't try. Local beers, unusual beers, farmhouse ciders - all have one

thing in common: distinctive taste and character, everything that the global blands of the multi-national breweries don't. And they'll probably be better value for money eleven times out of ten too!

So where can you find these beer festivals? In Herefordshire, CAMRA organises Beer on the Wye. Held each summer in Hereford city centre, this showcase event is held in a marquee on the banks of the River Wye at Hereford Rowing Club and combines fun events on the river with the very best of beer, cider, food and imaginative live music. Herefordshire's largest bar can boast beers of virtually every hue, description and strength from all across the British Isles. With over 100 real beers to choose from, and over 30 ciders and perries from Herefordshire cider producers alone, plus foreign and bottled beers, Beer on the Wye is rapidly establishing itself as one of the key annual events in the county. In 2005, over 1600 visitors drank over 6300 pints in just two and a half days – not bad going!

Perhaps you can't get along to Beer on the Wye, or you live further afield? Just over the border, CAMRA also annually organises successful beer and cider festivals in Worcester, Bromsgrove, Redditch, Shrewsbury, Bridgnorth, and Tewkesbury. The grand-daddy of them all is the national beer festival, held at London's prestigious

Earl's Court – the Great British Beer Festival which last August attracted 47,000 thirsty visitors, who consumed over 400 different draught real ales from over 200 different breweries, as well as cider, perry and bottled ales.

Want to know more? Locally, keep an eye open for information about Beer on the Wye. It's held at the beginning of July or the very end of June, and full details are always posted on www.herefordcamra.org.uk. Alternatively, for beer festivals further afield go on-line at www.camra.org.uk – there is bound to be one near to you.

LIFE OR DEATH IN THE COUNTRY -
THE FUTURE OF THE VILLAGE PUB

No one in CAMRA is trying to pretend that running a country pub is a bed of roses – far from it. Long anti-social hours for not a great financial return, is all too often the reward for the country publican. However, all is far from doom and gloom behind the bar out in the country. Increasingly, people are now recognising the value of the village pub. Many publicans and potential publicans see that running a country pub does have significant upsides: quality of life issues - such as making a living as the key member of a strong rural community, and the advantage of working and living in the country are just one or two perceived benefits. Further, there is increasingly a trend back to tripping out to country pubs once more – as more people have more free time, disposable income and a greater awareness of the countryside around us: this means more customers. Communities are becoming increasingly aware of the importance of their local pub too, and in some cases are even prepared to buy it and run it themselves! Therefore, against this improving backdrop, it is worrying to see that pubs are continuing to close at the rate of more than a six a week, although interestingly the overall trend of pub closures is now becoming increasingly an urban phenomenon.

What is being done to help country pubs? CAMRA believes it is important to support our country and village pubs. They are a vital part of our national heritage and our way of life: could you imagine a rural Britain on a fine summer's evening without the village pub? Without their local pub, many rural communities would be deprived of their last social amenity. All too often the school, shop, and post office have already gone, and the pub is the last social focal point in a community.

CAMRA has a whole series of national and local initiatives to promote pubs. Each February we organise the high-profile *National Pubs Week* – a major pan-industry campaign to promote pubs to non-users. This campaign represents a major financial commitment each year. Nearer to home, Herefordshire CAMRA produces this important guide - and there are many other local CAMRA Pub Guides similar to this one for other areas in the UK, all highlighting the virtues of our country pubs. Herefordshire CAMRA additionally produces free information leaflets, newsletter articles, and displays at our Beer & Cider Festival to further encourage local people and tourists to visit country pubs. These publications give public transport information and details of country pubs in 'bite-size' proportions – thus removing the perceived 'complications' of planning that trip out to a country pub. All of these supporting initiatives take time, volunteer effort and cost money - and please do remember CAMRA is not even the trade body responsible for the welfare of our country pubs! We are a national consumer organisation representing the views of pub-users – so why do we do this? The answer is quite simple: it would appear that no-one else appears to be the slightest bit interested!

So who should be supporting the cause of country pubs? The British Beer & Pub Association (BBPA) is the trade body that represents the British pub industry. So what does it say and do for country pubs? Mark Hastings, their national spokesmen, has gone on record in The Times to bemoan the difficulty faced by landlords in converting their pubs into private houses, due to the constraints of the planning process. It would appear the BBPA's answer is to make it easier to close our village pubs and asset-strip them. With Dracula now apparently in charge of the bloodbank at the BBPA, CAMRA would appear to be the sole organisation interested in the welfare of our pub heritage.

CAMRA needs to stay alive to these threats:

- Greedy breweries and pub-operating companies who buy country pubs at crazy prices, that ultimately means they have entirely unrealistic rental expectations for the location - inevitable closure of previously successful pubs will often follow.
- Publicans who fancy chancing their luck by selling off a pub off as a development opportunity for a fast buck, rather than offering it for sale as a pub first - as their predecessors have done for centuries before.
- Cynical opportunists seeking a twee country home at an affordable price, who find themselves 'frozen out' by a busy property market. They appear quite happy to target a village pub and don't give two hoots about closing it down in the process.

CAMRA strongly supports the efforts of our country landlords, and recognises the efforts they put in. Unfortunately - life being as it is - publicans come and go and pubs change hands. It isn't an easy trade, and running a country pub requires special skills from dedicated people. Not everyone has what it takes, and running a country pub ▶

IS YOUR LOCAL UNDER THREAT? GET IN TOUCH WITH US NOW!

Concerned that your pub is being closed? Worried that it isn't being offered for sale? We will help you. Herefordshire CAMRA can provide help and advice. Don't allow your local to be asset-stripped! Once it's gone, it's gone forever.

isn't for the half-hearted or ill-prepared. It is a sad fact of life that pub businesses fail from time to time, and CAMRA has no wish to place further obstacles in the way of those who have genuinely failed with their pub enterprise - and their dreams.

However, CAMRA will resist most vigorously the actions of the feckless and unscrupulous asset-strippers who prey on the misfortune of those publicans who have genuinely hit hard times. Rural asset-strippers are quite content to cynically use the business failure of the previous incumbent as an excuse to close and convert a pub into a private house, before considering the future of the pub and the wider community. Fortunately, to convert a pub into a private dwelling requires planning permission from the local council. This is where CAMRA comes in: we do not routinely object to every planning application to convert a pub into a private house - that would be to adopt an entirely unreasonable stance.

CAMRA will object and campaign against any planning application to convert a pub into a private house where no genuine effort has been made to find new owners (or operators) by marketing the pub for at least twelve months, and where is strong support for the it in the local community. National and local planning guidelines require

pub owners to do this in the first instance. Recently, Herefordshire CAMRA has prevented the conversion of the Red Lion at Kilpeck for these very reasons. This is just one of a number of recent planning successes. We'd rather have to not campaign on these matters, but whilst these threats remain we will face them up. In the past twelve months CAMRA has set up the Community Pubs Foundation, as separate organisation to support and advise local communities fighting to save their pubs (www.communitypubs.org.uk).

Come fill your Glass

The most easily recognised, and by far the most common method of dispense in the County, is the traditional hand pump or 'beer engine'. Fitted to the bar counter, this simple suction pump First patented by Joseph Bramah in 1797 was the earliest mechanical method of raising beer from the cellar to the bar. Each time the handle is pulled forwards, beer is drawn and dispensed from the nozzle. Each full stroke will deliver a third or half-pint measure, with short strokes used for topping up. The head is controlled through the use of swan-necks, fitted with a creamer which directs the beer into the bottom of the glass, the gas breaking out beneath the surface of the liquid and rising to the top in tighter formation.

The electric pump [P] that dispenses a metered quantity of beer, once a familiar sight in Banks's pubs, has all but disappeared.

Some rural pubs (Bulls Head, Craswall; Carpenters Arms, Walterstone; Yew Tree, Preston on Wye) serve beer straight from the cask by gravity [G], the cask being stillaged in a chilled area behind the bar. The disadvantage with this is that the beer can become warm, although nowadays this can be prevented using water-cooled saddles and insulating jackets.

LIVE & LET LIVE @ BRINGSTY COMMON

THE PUB THAT REFUSES TO DIE

Located high on the scenic expanses of Bringsty Common is the 16th-century ex-cider house that is known affectionately as the 'Live'. Boasting uninterrupted views towards the Malvern Hills, the simple and wonderfully unspoilt two-bar pub has always played

an important role in the rural dispersed community that makes up Bringsty Common. In the summer of 1996, the landlady dropped a bombshell: a planning application had been submitted that would see the unique pub converted into a private house. The pub would close forever.

Immediately, Herefordshire CAMRA got together with the locals to start a campaign to save the 'Live', and over the next few years successfully saw off three planning applications and an appeal hearing. At one stage CAMRA helped to raise over £158,000 in an attempt to buy the 'Live'. However, that ultimately wasn't necessary, and in 2002 a new owner bought the pub – someone who saw its true potential and wanted to re-open and develop it.

It was hoped that we would see the 'Live' return to the fold a few years back, but after various false dawns along the way, it now looks like the necessary renovation work will take place over the summer of 2006, with an opening date for later in the same year. The new landlady, Sue Dovey and her family, have some exciting plans for the place: they are looking to put a thatched roof back on the inn once more – it is probable that it lost its original thatch back in the early 19th Century, and they see the pub being very much back at the heart of its community.

Traditional British Ale
- Our Heritage

Real Ale is now almost universally accepted as a synonym for traditional British top-fermented ales. Brewed using malted barley, water, hops and yeast, it is finally stored in a vented cask, where a second fermentation creates a natural carbonation in the beer. The term also applies to naturally-conditioned bottled beers where the yeast sediment matures the beer in the bottle.

Although beer can be produced from almost any cereal crop, traditional brewing starts by malting barley, a process, which converts the starches in the grains into soluble sugar and makes them fermentable. The barley grains are steeped in water, thus initiating germination. This is allowed to continue for a few days before the grains are transferred to a kiln room where a high temperature prevents any further growth, and produces the different types of malt required for brewing. The more intense the kilning, the darker and bitterer the malt. With generations of knowledge, the specialist maltster is able to produce a wide palette of flavours and colours.

In the brewery, the malt is first cracked (lightly crushed) in a mill to produce a coarse powder called grist, and then mixed in the mash tun with hot water (referred to in the trade as liquor). This liquor has usually been treated to remove unsuitable chemicals, and minerals added to emulate the natural brewing waters of Burton-on-Trent. After an hour and a half's mashing the sugars from the grist are dissolved and a thick, sweet liquid, called wort is produced. This is then run into a copper while the grains are sprayed, or 'sparged', with more hot water. The spent grains are sold for cattle fodder. The wort is now boiled with hops in a copper. Hops help to preserve the beer although their main purpose is to impart bitterness and aroma, and like malt, come in many varieties. Some may be used to produce a high degree of bitterness, while others for their subtleness, introducing spicy, floral or citrus notes to the aroma and flavour.

After boiling, the wort is filtered through the spent hops in the hop back, cooled through heat-exchangers, before being run into fermenting vessels. When sufficiently cooled, the yeast is added, or 'pitched'. This micro-organism propagates itself by feeding on the sugars in the sweet wort, converting them into alcohol and carbon dioxide, a process called fermentation. Each strain of yeast has its own character and brewery chemists are careful to maintain consistency down many decades of brewing, taking care to eliminate the risk of contamination from wild yeast.

After a few days, the primary fermentation is over, and the rough beer is run into conditioning tanks where it continues to work. From here on, the real ale, keg and nitrokeg beers go their separate ways. The keg and nitrokeg are chilled, filtered and pasteurised, effectively killing off and removing any remaining living yeast. They are then injected with additional carbon dioxide - or mixed nitrogen and carbon dioxide - and sealed in kegs. On the other hand, the real ale is put into casks, a process known as 'racking'. Here 'finings', (the ground swim bladder from large fish, traditionally sturgeon) are added to ensure that, following the second fermentation in the cask, all the yeast is drawn to the bottom to leave a bright, clear beer ready for sale. Also, priming sugar may be added to encourage a vigorous secondary fermentation and sometimes dry hops to give extra aroma. The beer is now ready for dispatch.

Once in the pub cellar, the quality of your 'perfect pint' is then the responsibility of the licensee or his cellarman. As soon as possible the beer is stillaged, traditionally on its belly and held firmly by chocks, though they may now be found cradled in automatic tilting devices or stood on end, the beer being drawn through a syphon. The cask is first vented to release any excess pressure built up during transportation, and a tap is hammered into the bung-hole at the front end of the cask. A soft, porous wooden peg is inserted into the shive hole on top of the cask, allowing the vital secondary fermentation to take place, giving traditional beer greater maturity and palate. The resulting natural carbon dioxide gas escapes through the peg, whilst the beer drops bright; the yeast, hops and finings sinking to the bottom of the cask. After about 48 hours, a harder peg is used to stop the beer going flat.

Early attempts to prolong the life of beer on sale required the introduction of carbon dioxide via the spile hole. Applied under pressure, this had the effect of producing a fizzy keg-like product. This practice has been abandoned in favour of using a 'demand valve', by which the beer drawn off is replaced with

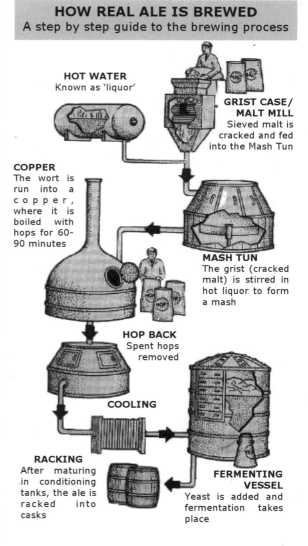

HOW REAL ALE IS BREWED
A step by step guide to the brewing process

HOT WATER
Known as 'liquor'

GRIST CASE/ MALT MILL
Sieved malt is cracked and fed into the Mash Tun

COPPER
The wort is run into a copper, where it is boiled with hops for 60-90 minutes

MASH TUN
The grist (cracked malt) is stirred in hot liquor to form a mash

HOP BACK
Spent hops removed

COOLING

RACKING
After maturing in conditioning tanks, the ale is racked into casks

FERMENTING VESSEL
Yeast is added and fermentation takes place

either carbon dioxide or preferably nitrogen without extraneous pressure. This slows down the oxidation and thereby the maturation process and may affect the flavour profile, but can make the difference in more-rural pubs to the viability of providing traditional cask conditioned ale. The use of gas in this way is contentious and does not meet with the approval of CAMRA.

A Question of Taste

A good beer can be judged by aroma, flavour and finish, and we are lucky that the beer brewed in our county is produced by brewers who care about their products, not by accountants who are only interested in making fizzy alcoholic water at the lowest possible cost. Why do they make so many? - it is a popular misconception that all beers taste the same. This could not be further from the truth - beer has a far more complex flavour than wine. Wine is based on a single ingredient - grapes, while beer is a fine balance of two - malt and hops. There are many different styles of malt and a wide range of cereal crops, not to mention different strains that can be used, and hop varieties are almost as numerous as those of grapes.

The description 'beer' covers a whole range of styles from a fresh, spritzy gueuze through to the dark, full-bodied winter ale and there is a rich and varied selection to please the palate and, as you travel around the county, to meet the need of the occasion.

Beer can be produced by either ale or lager style fermentation. Real ale is produced using yeasts that 'top ferment' at temperatures up to 22°C, producing the rich variety of flavours typically found in ale. After primary fermentation the ale is allowed to mature at 11-13°C in a cask where a slow secondary fermentation occurs. Lager, on the other hand, is produced by 'bottom fermenting' yeast at temperatures 6-14°C, then it should be conditioned for several weeks at about 0 – 1°C during which time the lager matures. Traditionally lager (the German word for store is lager – hence the name) style beers were brewed during the cooler winter months and then stored in cool cellars through the summer months.

Most of the beers brewed in the County of Herefordshire are English ales and this can be broken down further into various styles, although Shoe's Lin's Lager and Priessnitz from the Malvern Hills Brewery (just over the boundary) are brewed in the lager style.

Bitter, the most common beer style - and available from all of our local brewers - is usually brown, tawny, copper or amber coloured with medium to strong bitterness and light to medium malt character. Bitter grew out of Pale Ale, but its darker colour is due to the use of slightly darker malts such as crystal that give the beer fullness of palate. Best is a stronger version of Bitter but there is considerable crossover. Bitter falls into the 3.4% to 3.9% ABV band, with Best Bitter 4% upwards, but be warned - a number of brewers label their ordinary Bitters 'Best'. A further development of Bitter comes in the shape of Extra or Special Strong Bitters of 5% or more (local examples of this style include Dunn Plowman Crooked Furrow and Spinning Dog Mutts Nuts). With ordinary Bitter, look for a spicy, peppery and grassy hop character, a powerful bitterness, tangy fruit and juicy and nutty malt. With Best and Strong Bitters, malt and fruit character will tend to dominate, but hop aroma and bitterness are still crucial to the style, often achieved by 'late hopping' in the brewery - adding hops to casks as they leave for pubs.

India Pale Ale was first brewed in London and Burton-on-Trent for the colonial market. IPAs were strong in alcohol and high in hops: the preservative character of the hops helped keep the beers in good condition during long sea journeys. Beers with less alcohol and hops were developed for the domestic market and were known as **Pale Ale**. Look for juicy malt, citrus fruit and a big spicy, peppery, bitter hop character in Wild's Blonde, Spinning Dog Herefordshire Light Ale and Hereford Pale Ale from the Wye Valley Brewery.

Up until the 1950s, **Mild** was the most popular style. Developed in the 18th and 19th centuries with a lower hop character than porter or stout, it can be found in light (Shoes Norton Ale) or dark versions (Spinning Dog Mutleys Dark). Look for rich malty aromas and flavours with hints of dark fruit, chocolate, coffee and caramel, mild is generally of a lower strength (less than 4%ABV) but visitors to the Black Country may have encountered Sarah Hughes Dark Ruby Mild at 6%ABV.

Porter was a London style dating from the early in the 18th century. It got its name as a result of its popularity among London's street-market workers. Originally dark brown in colour, it was a blend of brown ale, pale ale and 'stale' or well-matured ale. At the time, a generic term in a brewery for the strongest beer was stout and so the strongest versions of Porter were known as Stout Porter, becoming simply **Stout** as time went on. Both styles have profound dark, roasted malt character with flavours including raisin and sultana fruit, coffee, liquorice and molasses, all underscored by hefty hop bitterness. Compare Spinning Dog Organic Oatmeal Stout with Dorothy Goodbody's Wholesome Stout, and Dunn Plowman Railway Porter (or Old Jake Stout) to appreciate the different styles locally.

Dating from the same era when England was often at war with France and it was the duty of patriots, usually from the upper classes, to drink ale rather than Claret. Thus **Barley Wine** had to be strong - often between 10% and 12% - and it was stored for as long at 18 months or two years. Having an almost vinous appearance in the glass, drinkers can expect massive sweet malt and ripe fruit of the pear drop, orange and lemon type, with darker fruits, chocolate and coffee if darker malts are used. Hop rates are generous and produce bitterness and peppery, grassy and floral notes. A fine example of this style can be found in Shoes Farriers Ale, one of the strongest beers brewed regularly and is also available in bottled version for the driver to savour at home.

A more recent innovation is **Golden Ale** developed by independent brewers in the 1980s in an attempt to win younger drinkers away from heavily-promoted lager brands. These are pale amber, gold, yellow or straw coloured beers with light to strong bitterness and a strong hop character which create a refreshing taste. The hallmark of this style is the biscuity, juicy malt character derived from pale malts, underscored by tart citrus fruit and peppery hops, often with the addition of hints of vanilla and sweetcorn. These beers are best served cool and can be exemplified by Dorothy Goodbody's Golden Ale, Spinning Dogs Celtic Gold, as well as Dormington Gold, and Ludlow Gold from Marches.

Links with much earlier times can be found in Dunn-Plowman Sting, which is sweetened with honey just as English ales would have been many centuries ago.

Real Ale in a Bottle

Real Ale in a Bottle is the next best thing, and the bottled equivalent, to the draught real ales you can enjoy at the pub. CAMRA has launched a logo "CAMRA says this is real ale" to clearly identify products that are the real thing: natural, living, bottle-conditioned beers. It is important to note that some cask-conditioned real ales, labelled to look the same as the cask product, do not undergo secondary fermentation once bottle - they're better than cans, but not the real thing!

CIDER - IT'S A FRUITY THING

Popular marketing speak would have us believe that the fizzy, yellow ciders on the bar or the colourless, highly-chilled liquid sold in bottles are real cider. This is not so.

- Real cider is as different from keg cider as real ale is from keg beer.
- Real cider and perry are traditional British drinks and should not be confused with poor imitations.

The good news for Herefordshire is that Cider is enjoying a resurgence and even more so that as the market for cider expands, so too does the willingness and opportunity to try the real thing. Since the last guide the number of outlets selling draught real cider or perry has increased by about 50% to fifty five.

Cider Making

Cider and perry orchards form a familiar scene on the Herefordshire landscape. Whether it is dwarf trees, laid out in regular rows by commercial growers and harvested by machine, or more traditional orchards of old trees on one of the many smallholdings, all require the ripe apples to be harvested from the beginning of September.

Natural cider is made in the traditional way. The fruit is crushed (called 'milling') into a mushy pulp which must be wrapped and sealed before pressing. Some producers, especially in Somerset, still press their apples through straw (horse hair was once used In Herefordshire). These are known as cheeses and the pressed pulp is ultimately used as animal feed, not only adding to the flavour of the meat but also adding something to the lifestyle of the beast. The extracted juice is then collected in vats, where fermentation takes place. The natural yeasts in the apples set to work, and the process can take several months. Most ciders ferment for the full period and are extremely dry. Sugar is added at fermentation, enabling the cider to reach around 14% alcohol by volume, and then water is added to dilute it down to a suitable strength.

The juice is then transferred to vats for maturation. Juices may be blended with other older juices to add character. Truly traditional cider making stops here and the cider is ready to serve, whilst keg cider is filtered (usually), pasteurised and served under gas pressure. This kills off much of the flavour and gives the fizzy mouthfeel of lemonade. Artificial flavourings and colourings may be added.

Serving Traditional Ciders

Ciders and perry are served either by handpump, or direct from a polypin (plastic container). Where demand is low, several pubs sell bottled versions from local producers. These can be either blends or single varietal types and it is now perfectly acceptable to chose one of these as a suitable alternative to wine with a meal.

Perry

The process for making perry is very similar to cider. But the supply of perry pears is limited, and not enough to fuel the potential growth in perry consumption - the mellower flavour of perry makes it attractive to a wider range of palates. In 2005, Dunkertons of Pembridge were presented with CAMRA's Pomona award for services to the industry, mainly occasioned by the planting of a new perry orchard opposite the cider mill.

The Clamour and a Fruitful Harvest

The Tradition of Wassailing

Since pagan times, it is has been customary throughout Herefordshire and many other parts of the West Country, to offer a tribute to the goddess Pomona in order to protect the orchards from evil spirits and to ensure a plentiful crop in the coming season. This traditional act is known as wassailing and comes from the Anglo-Saxon phrase, *"wes hal"* which means 'to be whole', 'be of good health'.

Farmers' family, workers and friends meet in the evening and proceed to the orchard, where a favoured tree is chosen to represent them all, and feted as a guardian of the orchard. A cider-soaked piece of toast or cake placed in a fork of the tree to attract birds such as the robin (spirits of the trees) and cider is poured over the lower branches and around its roots.

The trees are then rapped, buckets and pans are beaten, and shotguns fired through the top-most branches of the tree to ward off evil spirits. Fires are usually lit: one in the middle, known as the Fire of 'Eternal Renewal', circled by twelve smaller ones which are lit simultaneously. The tree is toasted with cider, followed by dancing and the singing of the special 'Wassail Song'. It is held that if the trees are not wassailed, then a poor harvest will follow.

Wassailing is traditionally performed on the eve of Twelfth Night (January 6th), Old Twelfth Night (January 17th) or less commonly Old Christmas Eve in the Julian calendar (January 5th). This came about as a result of eleven days being omitted from the beginning of 1752 when, by Act of Parliament, the nation switched from the Julian to the Gregorian calendar. In many parts of the country, however, the important ancient traditions were still celebrated on their appropriate days.

Besides Wassailing there are two further significant periods in the cider-making calendar.

Firstly, the month of May, when the orchards are filled with blossom and enthusiasts are welcomed to visit the orchards surrounding the Marcle ridge and around Bosbury and to sample the fruits of last years labours in the form of cider, perry or culinary delights made from orchard produce. It is also the time when the Cider Museum in Hereford holds a Cider & Perry Fayre which plays host to the International Cider & Perry Competition, when the very best of producers from around the world compete for these most prestigious of awards.

The second time of great activity is, of course, harvest time - centred around October. Apple Day is celebrated by Common Ground on the 21st and CAMRA has bestowed the title of 'Cider & Perry Month' on the whole of October. Opportunities abound now to see how traditional cider is made. Once again, the major centres are the seven parishes around Much Marcle which hold the Big Apple weekend, and the Cider Museum, hosts a Cider Making Festival. Related events are also held in Leominster and on Hereford Racecourse

HEREFORDSHIRE - A Pace for Enjoyment

Probably the most rural of English counties, Herefordshire is a haven of peace and tranquillity. Its easy pace of life and gentle rolling countryside is interspersed with charming 'black and white' villages, conjuring up an atmosphere that many would describe as typically and traditionally English. To the east, the picturesque market towns of Bromyard and Ledbury nestle below the Malvern Hills, while to the west the county becomes more Welsh, not only in appearance with its rugged hills and dramatic views, but also in its climate and its people. While on the rich red fertile plains that lie between can be found the world-renowned Herefordshire cattle and sheep but also the roll in a patchwork filled with apple orchards, hop fields, vineyards, woodlands and sparkling rivers. Herefordshire is also steeped in history, and today's idyllic landscapes belie this turbulent past, when cross-border raids and skirmishes were part of daily life amid the Marcher counties. Here among the ancient borderlands with Wales, the sites of Iron-age forts, Roman settlements and dramatically sited castles can only hint at their often-violent history.

At the heart of the county, both geographically and administratively, is the ancient City of Hereford. Strategically sited on the banks of the River Wye, with Cathedral status since 676AD, its streets are filled with pubs, interesting buildings and distinctive shops - many containing hidden surprises - which will reward any exploration on foot. The 11th Century Norman Cathedral, built to replace the one destroyed in 1055 when the Welsh sacked the city, houses the world-famous Mappa Mundi and the unusual chained library with some 1500 volumes of priceless books and manuscripts. Two of the city museums offer free admission, while the Cider Museum in Pomona place and the Waterworks museum at Broomy Hill make a modest charge - details are available from the City Tourist Information Office.

Herefordshire's market towns act as gateways to the county and all have something different to offer the visitor. On the western border, Kington has a wonderful timeless feel very typical of the Welsh Marches, while to the east, Bromyard and Ledbury have many traditional black and white timber-framed buildings considered to be so typical of the county. The two largest of the market towns lie on the A49: Leominster to the north of Hereford has a history dating back to the 7th Century and still retains much of its medieval and Tudor characteristics. The last ducking stool to be used in England can be found at the Priory Church, founded 1123. To the south, set on a high sandstone cliff overlooking a loop in the River Wye is the town of Ross, again with a rich heritage and an ideal centre for visiting the southern reaches of the Wye or the ancient lands of Archenfield.

The Black & White Village Trail is a 40 mile circular motor route through some of the prettiest villages and most beautiful landscape in England. The trail leads west from the ancient town of Leominster, through a rich landscape of orchards, hopyards and distant hills, taking in the most picturesque black and white villages along the way, as well as the little market town of Kington.

Each of the towns provides an excellent opportunity for shopping. Many businesses are still family run and offer a welcome alternative to the 'Anytown' cloned High Street. Local produce is widely available around the county from local stores, farmshops and the regular farmers' markets. And remember amongst our local produce you will find Cider, Perry, Herefordshire grape and fruit wines and, of course, hop products.

Herefordshire is the county for the outdoor enjoyment and large areas can be explored by those who enjoy walking, cycling or riding. More adventurous tastes such as canoeing, sailing, climbing, can be accommodated and specialist centres for mountain boarding and paint-balling can be found. There are opportunities for those inclined towards country pursuits with opportunities for pool or river fishing, and clay shooting.

Whether a serious historian or just a sightseer, there is much to see and visit. Iron-age forts, medieval castles churches in a myriad of building styles - and of course the pubs: not just for the beer, but for the insight into the heritage and lifestyle of the area. Herefordshire is a well kept secret that we like to share with 'Friends' and as you travel around the county, take the time to talk to those you meet on your way. Who knows? You may come to enjoy the pace.

Herefordshire on Foot or in the Saddle

For open hill walking the high land all along the western borders with its splendid views across the county is the obvious choice. The Offa's Dyke National Trail runs just over the Welsh border along the Black Mountains and also between Hay on Wye and Kington. Nearby, just to the east of the Black Mountains, the Golden Valley offers some of the most beautiful walking to be found in the County. A section of the Herefordshire Trail follows the riverside meadows of the peaceful unspoilt River Dore and lead enticingly up the wooded western hillsides where spectacular views are to be had. Dore Abbey and Arthur's Stone lie along this route.

The beautiful Wye Valley must also lay claim to be one of Herefordshire's most attractive walking areas and the Wye Valley Walk follows the whole river as it's long journey crosses the shire between the two Welsh counties of Powys and Gwent. The most dramatic scenery being found to the south of Ross on Wye around the area of Symonds Yat with its limestone gorge and panoramic view from Yat Rock.

The western side of the Malvern Hills and the countryside around Ledbury provides beautiful woodland, superb views and plenty of Herefordshire's peace and tranquillity. This part of the county is mainly arable and here the Herefordshire Trail or Three Choirs Way will pass hop-farms, orchards and vineyards.

A completely different feel greets visitors to Mortimer country, that area between Kington and Ludlow once ruled by one of the most powerful mediaeval families in the land. Limestone tops punctuate a mixture of gentle pastures and extensive forests. Here the ancient hill forts at Croft Ambrey and Wapley can be found. Five loop walks connect with the Trail, providing descents from the high ridges and opportunities for shorter circular walks.

As well as the long-distance walks described below, many shorter circular walks exist. These are readily available in book or leaflet ▶

TOURIST INFORMATION CENTRES

Tourist Offices marked on maps in this guide:

Hereford City	(01432) 268430
Leominster	(01568) 616460
Ross-on-Wye	(01989) 562768
Ledbury	(01531) 636147
Bromyard	(01885) 482038
Kington (summer only)	(01544) 230778
Queenswood	(01568) 797842

Other offices:

Hay-on-Wye	(01497) 820144
Ludlow	(01584) 875053
Malvern	(01684) 892289

Tourist information at www.herefordshire.com

form and also appear as a regular feature in the local press. Various societies including the Ramblers Association offer 'Led Walks' at least once a week and Herefordshire Council put together a twice yearly 'Walking Festival' in June and over the Christmas period.

For those that have a preference for pedal power, a free leaflet entitled The Herefordshire Cycle Guide, published by Hereford-shire Council is available from Tourist Offices and libraries, or alternatively, on the internet, just log on to www.getcycling.info/herefordshire. As well as plenty of peaceful back lanes to explore, part of the National Cycle Network links Ledbury with Leominster. Recently a second cider cycle route linking the Black & White villages has been added to the Ledbury - Marcle route.

If, on the other hand you prefer four legs beneath your seat a long distance bridle way has been developed by the British Horse Society between Tedstone Wafre in the North east following bridle paths and quiet lanes across the width of the county as it heads towards the Brecon Beacons. A list of B&Bs and Guest houses that can provide accommodation for both horse and rider are available through the Tourist Information Centres. There are numerous yards around the county who can provide stabling or provide an opportunity for riding on an hourly, half day or full day basis for those without their own mount.

Herefordshire Trail

The 154 mile route was devised by members of Herefordshire Ramblers and launched in 2005. It is a Circular walk completely within the county boundaries and passes through farmlands, woodlands, waterside and bracing ridges as it visits all of the market towns.

Wye Valley Walk (136 miles) Chepstow to Plylimon, Hafren Forest
It originally ran from Chepstow to Rhayader, but was extended to the source of the river in 2002. The route criss-crosses the border of England and Wales, as it takes the walker through some of the finest scenery in the British Isles - dramatic limestone gorges, the rolling country-side of Herefordshire and the uplands of mid Wales.

Mortimer Trail (30 miles) Ludlow (Shropshire Way/ Marches Way) to Kington (Offa's Dyke Path)
The Trail through an area once dominated by the one of the most powerful Norman families, the Mortimers, was fully opened in 2002. It includes some strenuous climbs as it crosses a succession of hills and ridges and limestone tops between the Teme, Lugg and Arrow river valleys,

Marches Way (204 miles) Chester to Cardiff (signed in Cheshire only)
A lengthy route linking Chester and Cardiff, two former Roman forts, through the borderlands of England and Wales. Includes numerous historic cities and towns such as Shrewsbury, Leominster and Abergavenny

The **Offa's Dyke Path** takes its name from the 8th Century king Offa, who built an earthwork to define the English Welsh border and keep out the Celts. It follows the Welsh side of the county border from Pandy to Knighton only crossing it to enter Kington.

The **Three Choirs Way** provides a long distance footpath between Gloucester, Hereford and Worcester, with a theme linking the walk and the Music Festival celebrated at the three Cathedrals for over 300 years. From Hereford both routes lead east entering Worcestershire over Bringsty Common, and Gloucestershire through Much Marcle.

TO THE PUB – USING PUBLIC TRANSPORT

It isn't immediately apparent that public transport is a viable way of exploring Hereford-shire's pubs, but you might just be pleasantly surprised. Have a look at what you can do, before you jump in the car and head for the pub!

Herefordshire may have the fewest number of railway stations for any of England's 'shire' counties, (there being only four of them at Colwall, Ledbury, Leominster and, of course Hereford), however, for a very rural county it does enjoy a surprisingly regular train service with services on most routes being typically hourly (and often better) - and they all operate until late at night. Services can get a little thinner on a Sunday. This guide has marked all the locations of the rail stations on the town maps. For de-tailed information on train times and fares, you can pick up timetable leaflets at Here-ford station - alternatively you can either ring National Rail Enquiries on 08457 48 49 50 (24-hour service) or go online at www.nationalrail.co.uk.

With the cutbacks in recent years to bus services in and around Hereford - particularly those more useful services in the evening, your bus options at night are limited to a few key bus routes. Towns and larger villages that have the benefit of good evening bus services to/from Hereford include Kington, Ledbury, Leominster, Madley, Ross-on-Wye, Wellington and Weobley – and the many smaller places in between. How-ever, if you are able to travel out during the day, then your options are greatly im-proved with a selection of services available to many smaller places. This guide sets out which places have viable bus services on page 83 to help you plan that journey to the pub by bus. For further information on bus times across the county, either ring Traveline on 0870 608 2 608 or go online at www.herefordshire-buses.tbctimes.co.uk

Herefordshire Council also produce useful local guides covering the county's bus and train information, and these are available from the various Tourist Information Centres around the county (listed on page 21)

ABBEYDORE — C6
Neville Arms
HR2 0AA On B4347
☎ (01981) 240319
11-late; 12-late Sun
Courage Directors; guest beer

Large roadside house named after the Neville family, Marquesses of Abergavenny who built the pub in 1907. The 'L' shaped bar has a games area with pool table, plus an area furnished with sofas, and there is a separate restaurant. The front garden offers good views of the Golden Valley with the 12th century Dore Abbey nearby. Bottled local cider (Gwatkins Cider & Scrumpy) is available, and the guest beer is from Wye Valley. All day bar snacks are complemented by contemporary cuisine with Sunday carvery in the restaurant.

🏨 ⊛ 🍴 🌑 🕭 Å ♣ P ✂

ALLENSMORE — C6
Three Horseshoes
HR2 9AS On B4348 near A465 junction
☎ (01981) 570329
11.30-3, 6.30-11; 12-11 Sun
St Austell Tribute; Wye Valley Butty Bach; guest beer (occasional)

A much-modernised timber-framed pub with a friendly welcoming atmosphere set back from the main road. Although having a single central bar, the old timbers break up the space into a public bar area with pool table, lounge and restaurant. Very popular for its food, the Three Horseshoes serves traditional, home-prepared bar snacks and full à la carte meals. Children are welcome. The guest beer is usually from a regional brewery.

🏨 ⊛ 🍴 🌑 🕭 ♣ P

Tram Inn
HR2 9AN On B4348
No real ale or cider

Run-of-the-mill roadside pub by a railway level crossing. The opening hours are erratic.

ALMELEY — B4
Bells Inn
HR3 6LF In village OS 334515
☎ (01544) 327216
12-3 (not Tue,Thu), 7-11; 12-11 Sat, Sun
Wye Valley Bitter; guest beer

From the car park, where horses may be seen at the hitching rail, this delightful stone-built village pub is entered through the erstwhile jug and bottle. Very popular with the locals, it has a large low-ceilinged bar and a second, non-smoking, room which doubles as family room and dining area. Outside is a double petanque piste. Traditional, home-prepared meals are served Thu to Sat evenings and roasts (booking necessary) on Sunday lunchtimes. The guest beer is generally from local brewers. Live music some Saturday evenings.

🏨 ⊛ ⊛ 🌑 🕭 🕭 ♣ P ✂

ASHPERTON — F5
Hopton Arms
HR8 2SE On A417, S of village
☎ (01531) 670520
www.hoptonarms.co.uk
12-3, 6-11; 12-3, 6.30-10.30 Sun
Draught Bass; Flowers Original; Woods Parish

Large, red brick roadside pub, tastefully refurbished with lounge and separate dining area. Outside is a large garden with play area. Campers and caravans welcome. Food is traditional English and a takeaway service is available.

🏨 ⊛ 🍴 🌑 🕭 Å ♣ P

ASTON CREWS — F7
Pennyfarthing
Aston Ingham, HR9 7LW On B4222
☎ (01989) 750366
12-3 (not Mon), 6-11; 12-3 Sun (closed eve),
Greene King Abbot; Wadworth 6X

There are fine views of the Herefordshire countryside from the garden of this rural pub. Much altered by refurbishment, the pub is open plan with a lounge containing an old well shaft, and a restaurant area divided into alcoves. A wide choice of food is on offer with sandwiches, separate lunch and evening menus plus fish specials. Children are welcome and there are full disabled facilities. Closed Sun eve and Mon eve in winter. This pub will shortly be free of tie and the beer range may change.

⊛ 🌑 🕭 P

AYMESTREY — C2
Riverside Inn
HR6 9ST On A4110, in village

☎ (01568) 708440
www.theriversideinn.org
11-3, 6-11; 12-3, 6-10.30 Sun
Wye Valley HPA; guest beer

Always a popular venue for evening and week-end diners, the Riverside does not neglect drinkers, with its stylishly-furnished bar areas and separate restaurant. Using local meat and home-grown produce, an interesting menu of well-presented dishes is available, with the accent on traditional English cuisine. The guest beer is from local breweries. Delightfully situated on the River Lugg, with its own mile of fishing rights, it is close to the Mortimer Trail footpath and a number of circular walks. Closed Sun eve and Mon in winter.

🏠 ❄ 🛏 ◑ ▶ P ⚋

BAILEY LANE END   F7

Wonky Donkey
HR9 5TR 1 mile S of A40 at Ryeford
OS 643203
☎ (01989) 750954
7-11 (not Mon); 12-3; 7-10.30 Sun
Whittingtons Cats Whiskers

This is a genuine old-style pub that has changed very little for many years, taking its name from the donkeys that took up residence in 2000. Situated on the edge of the Forest of Dean, the attractive terraced garden has good views of the surrounding countryside. The main bar area is small, with a dining room to one side. The home-made food includes Sunday roast and dinners can be served to parties to order.

Q ❄ 🛏 ▶ ◰ ♿ ♣ P

BARTESTREE   E5

New Inn
HR1 4BX On A438, in village

☎ (01432) 850212
5-11; 12-11 Sat, Sun
Marstons Bitter; guest beer

Built as a substantial private house in 1870 and only becoming a pub in 1954, the New Inn is noted for its striking red brick Gothic appearance. It also contains many reminders, most notably in the cellar, of the original owner, William Godwin, who also owned the famous local tile works. There is a games bar with pool table, a main public bar, and a comfortable lounge which is served through a hatch from the main bar. Occasional live music.

🏠 Q ➤ ❄ 🛏 ◑ ▶ ◰ 🚌 ♣ P ⚋

BELMONT   D5

Three Counties Hotel (Mundi`s Bar)
HR2 7BP On A465
☎ (01432) 299995
www.threecountieshotel.co.uk
5.30-11 daily

Brains Reverend James

Large, comfortable modern hotel bar with large screen TV and attractive pond and garden outside. Located on the southern fringe of Hereford, it caters for families and offers a full à la carte menu.

Q ❄ 🛏 ▶ ♿ P

BISHOPS FROME   F4

Chase Inn
WR6 5BP On B4214, in village
☎ (01885) 490234
11-midnight; 11-1am Thu-Sat; 12-midnight Sun
Banks's Original, Bitter; Marstons Bitter

An imposing pub facing the village green. The main lounge bar has a large fireplace, some original features and bare brickwork. The traditional public bar offers darts and pool. Homely and friendly, the pub serves traditional meals with roasts on Sunday. No food Sun or Mon eves.

❄ 🛏 ◑ ▶ ◰ ♿ 🚌 ♣ P

Green Dragon
WR6 5BP Just off B4214, in village
☎ (01885) 490607
5-11; 12-11 Fri, Sat; 12-4, 7-11 Sun

Taylor Golden Best; Theakston Best Bitter; Wye Valley Butty Bach; house beer; guest beer

A welcome return for this iconic pub - once a 70s and 80s mecca for real ale, and now back in its rightful place under enthusiastic new ownership as a top beer pub. A splendid unspoiled 17th Century low-beamed multi-roomed inn, it has a warren of flagstone bars and an inglenook fireplace forming the centrepiece of the main bar (there's a real fire in every room). To the left is a TV and function room-cum restaurant. Conversation is allowed to rule. Food is served (not Sundays) with steaks a speciality. Draught local cider is served in summer.

🏚 ✿ ◑ ▶ 🎪 ♣ 🍺 P

BODENHAM — D4

England's Gate Inn
HR1 3HE Just off A417, in village
☎ (01568) 797286
11-11; 12-10.30 Sun

Wood Shropshire Lad; Wye Valley Bitter, Butty Bach; guest beer

Seventeenth century black and white inn that has been opened out internally and extensively modernised, but still retains fine original timbers and a flagstone floor. The single, large bar contrasts with a number of more intimate nooks and crannies. The guest beer is usually from a local brewery. This pub has a strong following for its excellent, affordable pub food served weekdays with traditional lunch on Sundays (no food Sun eve).

🏚 ✿ ◑ ▶ ♿ 🎪 P ✗

BOSBURY — G5

Bell Inn
HR8 1PS On B4220, in village
☎ (01531) 640285
7-11 Mon; 5-11 Tue-Fri; 11-11 Sat; 12-10.30 Sun

Hancocks HB; guest beer

Pleasant black-and-white timber-framed village pub situated opposite the church. It has a public bar and games area popular with locals for cards in particular, a lounge bar with an interesting fireplace and a separate restaurant. Traditional home-prepared food is served, except on Sunday evenings and Mondays.

🏚 ✿ ◑ ▶ 🍺 🎪 ♣

BREDENBURY — E3

Barneby Inn
HR7 4TF On A44, in village
☎ (01885) 482233
11-3, 6-11; 12-3, 7-10.30 Sun

Wye Valley Bitter; guest beer

An impressive Georgian house that became a pub (the New Inn) in Victorian times but was more recently renamed after a local family. The friendly bar is decorated with a wide range of old implements and tools associated with country crafts. The good value food includes traditional bar snacks, carvery and à la carte menu. Vegetarians are well catered for. Set in half an acre of gardens, this is an ideal place to take the children. Guest beer is from regional or micro breweries.

Q ✿ 🍴 ◑ ▶ ♿ ♣ P

BREDWARDINE — B5

Red Lion Hotel
HR3 6BJ On B4352, in village
☎ (01981) 500303
www.redlion-hotel.com
12-3 (not winter), 7-11(not Mon,Tue in winter); 12-3, 7-11 Sat; 12-3, 7-10.30 (not winter eve) Sun

Greene King IPA; Marstons Pedigree or Tetley Imperial; guest beer

An imposing red brick hotel overlooking the River Wye, on which it has eight miles of fishing rights. On the Wye Valley Walk footpath, it consists of a panelled lounge, a non-smoking snug with fishing memorabilia, and a restaurant. Traditional home-prepared pub food is served - snacks at lunchtime and meals in the evenings. Curry night Thursday.

🏚 Q ✿ 🍴 ◑ ▶ P ✗

BRIDGE SOLLERS — C5

Lord Nelson Inn
HR4 7JN On A438
☎ (01981) 590208

A comfortable roadside pub with a single long bar with exposed beams and a restaurant and function room. Closed at the time of printing, the Nelson typically offers real ale and food.

BRIMFIELD   D2

Roebuck
SY8 4NE   In village, just E of A49 and S of A456
☎ (01584) 711230
11.30-3, 6.30-11; 12-3, 7-10.30 Sun
Banks's Bitter; guest beer

This unusual pub has two separate bars and a restaurant. The light oak-panelled bar has a real fire with interesting old local pictures, drawings and maps. Sandwiches and bar snacks are available at lunchtimes together with an imaginative menu of locally-sourced restaurant meals in the evenings (not Sunday), for which booking is advised.

🏚 Q ✿🖂 ◖ ◗ ⬚ ♿ P ✄

BRINGSTY COMMON   F3

Live & Let Live
WR6 5UW   Down track onto common, S of A44
Unspoiled 16ᵗʰ Century ex-cider house of great character. Closed since 1996, this beautifully-situated pub on the common has been the subject of four planning enquiries. It is anticipated that this fantastic pub will reopen in late 2006. See report p13.

BRITISH CAMP   G5

Malvern Hills Hotel
Jubilee Drive, WR13 6DW   On A449
☎ (01684) 540690
www.malvernhillshotel.co.uk
10-11 daily
Malvern Hills Black Pear; Wye Valley Bitter, Hereford Pale Ale; guest beer

Large landmark hotel located high on the Malvern Hills, near the British Camp Hill Fort. Benefitting from much investment by new owners, it is very popular with locals and particularly with walkers (dogs and well-behaved children welcome - the latter until 5.30pm). There is a genuine commitment to quality cask beers - five pumps adorn the main bar, with guest beers from local breweries. An airy restaurant offers quality dining, along with imaginative and affordable quality bar meals in the main bar. A new conservatory, along with outside seating,

makes this an ideal venue for a fine day. Function room and conference facilities available.

🏚 ✿🖂 ◖ ◗ ♿ ♣ P ✄

BROMYARD   F3

Bay Horse
19-21 High Street, HR7 4AA
☎ (01885) 482600
11-11(midnight Fri, Sat)
Spinning Dog Mutley's Revenge; Wye Valley Bitter, Butty Bach, Thatchers Traditional Cider

The timber framing reveals that this attractive pub in the town centre was once two buildings, dating from the 17th century. Having recovered completely from a ruthless 1980s refurbishment this pub now has great character. Original wood panelling, cosy seating and cushioned benches, make for comfort and encourage conversation. There is a pleasant patio and garden to the rear. Freshly prepared bar and restaurant meals are served. Families are welcome.

✿🖂 ◖ ◗ 🚌 ♣ 🚲 P

Crown & Sceptre
7 Sherford Street, HR7 4DL
☎ (01885) 482441
12-3 (not Mon, Tue), 5.30-11(midnight Thu- Sat); 12-3, 7-10.30 Sun
Black Sheep Bitter; Marstons Pedigree; guest beer, Addlestones Cider

A hotel of sixteenth century origin with a Georgian red brick façade and pleasant open plan interior divided into games area, lounge and restaurant. Outside is a large, attractive garden, with children's play area and views over Bromyard Downs. Locally sourced, freshly prepared food is served (not Sun-Tue eves). Modern facilities include a fully-equipped disabled toilet.

🏚 ✿🖂 ◖ ◗ ♿ 🚌 ♣ 🚲 P

Falcon Hotel
4 Broad Street, HR7 4BT
☎ (01885) 483034
11-3, 6-11; 12-3, 7-10.30 Sun
Brains Reverend James; Wye Valley Bitter

For many years this relatively unspoilt 17th century hotel was rendered over, but the plasterwork was later removed to reveal the impressive timbers. A centre of Bromyard life over the centuries. Behind a modern glass entrance door lies a comfortable bar, and restaurant plus conference facilities. Meals include bar snacks, and à la carte. Families are welcome.

🏠 Q ❀ ⇄ ◖◗ ♿ 🚌 P

Holly Tree
Stourport Road, HR7 4NT On B4203, N of town
☎ (01885) 488881
11-3, 6-11; 11-11 Sat; 12-10.30 Sun

This out-of-town pub, with a public bar, a small lounge and a large restaurant, is expected to have reopened when this guide is published and to be offering real ale and food.

Hop Pole Hotel
The Square, HR7 4BP
☎ (01885) 482449
12-11; 12-10.30 Sun
No real ale or cider

An impressive, Regency-style town hotel, over-looking the market square.

Kings Arms
45 High Street, HR7 4AE

☎ (01885) 483226
11-midnight daily
Tetley Bitter

A fine timber-framed building, dating from 1520, that boasts the largest chimney in the area. Inside there are two oak-beamed bars, with a friendly atmosphere: the rear bar has a pool table. Traditional pub food is available, freshly prepared and using local produce, including a children's menu. Families are welcome until 8pm. Sky Sports is shown on TV.

🏠 Q ☎ ❀ ◖ ⊟ ♿ 🚌 ♣ P

Monty's
1 Broad Street, HR7 4BS
☎ (01885) 482395
12-11 (1am Fri, Sat); 12-10.30 Sun
Single changing beer

This former draper's shop is now a deceptively large bar, tastefully decorated in a modern light style. A room to the rear contains a pool table and large screen TV. Catering for a mixed clientele during the week, a DJ draws a younger crowd on Friday and Saturday evenings. A function room is available for hire. Bar snacks served. Real ale availability is variable.

🚌 ♣

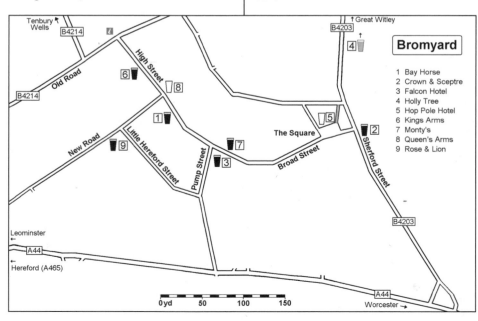

1 Bay Horse
2 Crown & Sceptre
3 Falcon Hotel
4 Holly Tree
5 Hop Pole Hotel
6 Kings Arms
7 Monty's
8 Queen's Arms
9 Rose & Lion

Queen's Arms
30 High Street, HR7 4AE
☎ (01885) 482281
No real ale or cider

A fine 400 year old timber-framed building, with an 18th century frontage.

Rose & Lion
5 New Road, HR7 4AJ
☎ (01885) 482381
11-3, 5-11; 11-midnight Fri & Sat; 12-midnight Sun
Wye Valley Bitter, Hereford Pale Ale, Butty Bach; guest beer: Westons Old Rosie Cider

One of Wye Valley's two tied houses, it is known affectionately as the 'Rosie'. Situated just off the High Street, this very traditional and unspoiled three-roomed pub has all the necessary ingredients: a friendly public bar, a cosy lounge, a good buzz and a a pleasant garden in which to drink good ale. It enjoys a loyal following amongst locals, whilst always welcoming visitors. A great pub for traditional pub games, a folk jam session is held on Sunday evenings. Rent for the garden is paid annually to Wye Valley in home-grown parsnips.

Q ✿⌂🚪✚🐾 P

BROMYARD DOWNS   F3
Royal Oak
Norton, HR7 4QP Off B4203 OS 671559
☎ (01885) 482585
11.30-2.30, 6-11; 12-3, 6-10.30 Sun
Hook Norton Hooky Best

Large multi-roomed, refurbished timber-framed pub with separate bars and restaurant, and a more utilitarian brick-built single-floor extension that serves as a function room. Outside there are patio and extensive garden drinking areas, and a spacious children's play area enjoying views towards Bromyard. Meals are not served on Monday evenings.

🏨 Q ✿◑▶♿✚ P

BUSH BANK   C4
Bush Inn
HR4 8EH On A4110
☎ (01432) 830206
12-2, 7-11 daily
Single changing beer

Welcoming establishment with a good local reputation for its home made traditional food. Previously a beer house called the Corners Inn, the Bush has been modernised and enlarged without losing its original character and rural charm. It now has two lounges, one with the original stone fireplace, a dining area and function room. Beer is from the Wye Valley range.

Q ✿◑▶♿🚪 P ✄

CANON PYON   D4
Nags Head
HR4 8NY On A4110, in village
☎ (01432) 830252
12-2.30 (not Mon), 6.30-11; 12-2.30, 6-11; 11.30-3.30, 6.30-10.30 Sun
Greene King Abbot

The large single bar in this 17th century building has original timbers, flagstone floor and feels very cosy with its real fire. The bar and the separate restaurant offer a range of home prepared food, from bar snacks to a full à la carte menu and a carvery on Sundays. Food is not served on Sunday or Monday evenings. Home of the Wye Valley Brewery in the mid 80s. Outside is a large adventure playground.

🏨 ✿⌂◑▶♿🚪 P

CAREY   E6
Cottage of Content
HR2 6NG In village OS 564310
☎ (01432) 840242
www.cottageofcontent.co.uk
12-3, 6.30-11 (closed Mon); 12-3, 6.30-10.30 (summer) Sun
Hook Norton Hooky Best; Wye Valley Butty Bach; guest beer (summer): Weston's Bounds Brand; Broome Farm Cider (summer)

A truly beautiful old part black and white building in idyllic surroundings - a real classic country pub. There has been a pub here since 1485, when, apparently, one of the three labourers' cottages for the Mynor family had an ale and cider parlour. Now there are two-bars and a separate restaurant. Although food of high quality predominates, drinkers are welcome. Booking is advised at most times for the freshly prepared bar snacks at lunchtime and à la carte in the evening. There is a large garden on the hillside to the rear.

🛏 ❀☕◖◗🍺 🐾 P

CLEHONGER — D5

Seven Stars
HR2 9SL On B4349, at E edge of village
☎ (01432) 277274
No real ale or cider

Two-bar roadside locals' establishment on the edge of the village.

CLODOCK — B7

Cornewall Arms
Longtown, HR2 0PD
☎ (01873) 860677
No real ale or cider

A tiny, unspoilt pub of great character, resplendent with a serving hatch that (sadly) serves no real ale, but does offer local bottled cider - Gwatkins Yarlington Mill and Golden Valley. Of great interest to pub historians. Games include darts, table skittles and quoits.

COLWALL — G5

Chase Inn
Chase Road, WR13 6DJ Off B4218, signed 'British Camp' OS 766431
☎ (01684) 540276
11.30-3, 5-11; 11.30-11 Sat, 12-10.30 Sun
Bathams Bitter; Hobsons Best Bitter; Woods Shropshire Lad; guest beers (2), Westons 1st Quality cider

Two-bar freehouse, located in a wooded backwater on the western slopes of the Malvern Hills, comprising a discrete lounge and a comfortable bar with pool table, and much interesting furniture and curios - where conversation always predominates. The secluded garden to the rear enjoys superb views across Herefordshire towards the Welsh Hills. The pub is very much beer-first (under the same ownership as the nearby, award-winning Nag's Head in Mal-

vern) and is well worth the 25 minute uphill walk from Colwall railway station. Booking is essential for the Sunday roast - no food Sun, Mon eves.

Q ❀◖☕🍺 🐾 🐾 P ✗

Colwall Park Hotel
Walwyn Road, WR13 6QG On B4218
☎ (01684) 540000
www.colwall.com
11-3, 6-11; 12-3, 7-10.30 Sun
Wye Valley Bitter; guest beer

Sedate and plush, but informal bar in an upmarket hotel in the centre of the village, with all the usual facilities - restaurant, conference and function room etc. The latter has a private bar - no real ale but can be taken through. Convenient for railway station and an excellent starting point for a walk on the Malvern Hills. Bar snacks and meals freshly prepared from local ingredients.

🛏 ❀☕◖◗ ♿ ⇌ 🍺 P

Crown
Walwyn Road, WR13 6QP On B4218
☎ (01684) 541074
11-3, 6 (5.30 Fri) -11; 12-11 Sat; 12-10.30 Sun
Brains Reverend James; Greene King IPA; Tetley Bitter

Two-bar pub, across the road from the railway station, with a lounge area to the front, and a spacious public bar with pool table to the rear. Home-cooked bar snacks, daily specials and à la carte meals are served in a separate dining area. This pub was changing hands at the time of this book going to print – please check for details.

🛏 ❀◖◗ ♿ ⇌ 🍺 🐾 P

Wellington
Chances Pitch, WR13 6HW, On A449, near B4218 junction
☎ (01684) 540269
12-3 (not Mon), 6.30 -11; 12-3 Sun
Goffs Tournament; guest beer

Situated in open country, on the main Ledbury-Malvern road near the Colwall turn, this much extended, multi-level building has a split-level main drinking area with dining to the rear. Lately considered only as a 'food pub', new owners are moving real beer and drinkers very much back up the agenda. It offers a more relaxed dining experience with a full range of meals - from full dining to 'beer snacks' pitched at £1.50 aimed at casual drinkers. Closed Sunday nights and all day Mondays.

🍺 Q ❁ ◖◗ 🚃 P

Yew Tree
Walwyn Road, WR13 6ED On B4218
☎ (01684) 540498
12-2, 7.30 -11; 12-3, 7.30-10.30 Sun
Banks's Bitter; guest beer

A spacious two-bar, but semi open-plan village local at the lower (Colwall Green) end of the village run by the same landlady for over 30 years and still retaining some fascinating 1950's decor. The bar area has a pool table. The friendly locals enjoy watching sport on TV. The beer is served through an interesting old beer engine.

🍺 Q ❁ 🔲 ⇌ 🚃 ♣ P 🍴

Bull`s Head
HR2 0PN On Longtown to Hay-on-Wye road OS 278360
☎ (01981) 510616
www.thebullsheadpub.com

11-3, 6-11; 11-11 Sat; 12-6 Sun

Wye Valley Butty Bach; guest beer

Remote ex-drovers' inn that spent 125 years in the same family up to 1999. A high quality refurbishment left the remarkable small main bar totally unaltered - a veritable time capsule, with its sloping flagstone floor, settle, range, peeling wallpaper and serving hatches - from where ale is drawn from the cask. Two further rooms are provided to enjoy the exciting range of food,

(booking advisable). Ideally located for walking nearby Hay Bluff and Offa's Dyke Path. En-suite B&B and camping, plus a horse corral for riders. The garden is ideal for families. Guest beer usually from Spinning Dog, with five ciders from Gwatkins and Westons.

🍺 Q ➘ ❁ 🛏 ◖◗ 🔲 Δ ♣ 🍺 ⚬

Crown Inn
HR4 8HL In village
☎ (01544) 318063
12-2.30 (not Mon), 7-11; 12-3, 7-11 Fri & Sat; 12-10.30 Sun

Black Sheep Bitter; Shepherd Neame Spitfire

The Crown is very much a community pub, encouraging the holding of meetings and functions by local organisations and fielding several pub game teams. Originally a 17th century black and white coaching inn, before the village was bypassed, it has been refronted and much altered although lots of beams remain visible in the two-bars inside. Traditional English food and bar snacks are available. The beer range changes from time to time.

🍺 Q ❁ ◖◗ 🔲 ♿ ♣ P ⚬

Railway Inn
HR1 3JP NE of A49   OS 512511
☎ (01568) 797053
11-3 (not Tue), 6-11 Tue-Fri; 11.30-2.30, 6.30-11 Sat; 12-3.30, 7-10.30 Sun

Wye Valley Bitter, Butty Bach; guest beer

Large modernised, split-level pub on slopes of Dinmore Hill originally built for workers on the adjacent tunnel on the Hereford-Shrewsbury railway line. Views from the large gardens extend across the Lugg Valley to the Malverns. The public and lounge bars are complemented by an upstairs dining room. An eclectic mix of cuisine is offered, home prepared from local ingredients. Opening times can be erratic (closed Sun eve in winter).

🍺 ❁ ◖◗ 🔲 ♿ P

King's Head
HR6 0RX On A44
☎ (01568) 760560
12-2.30, 6.30-midnight (1 Fri, Sat); 12-11 Sat; 12-2.30, 6-11 Sun

Greene King IPA

This friendly and well kept 17th century road-side pub in beautiful surroundings, has a single bar with snug, discrete games area and a separate restaurant which at times doubles as a local meeting room. Opening times, choice of real ale and provision of food are subject to change due to impending change of licensee.

🏠 Q ❀ ◑ ⅃ ⅙ ♣ P

DORSTONE — B5

Pandy Inn

HR3 6AN   Signed off B4348   OS 313416
☎ (01981) 550273
www.pandyinn.co.uk
12-3, 6-11 (not Mon in winter); 12-11 Sat; 12-3, 6.30-10.30 Sun

Wye Valley Butty Bach; guest beer, Gwatkins Cider (summer)

Set opposite the village green, the Pandy has a history dating back to the 12th century. Although opened out, the discrete areas give a welcoming feel with both timber-framing and exposed stone walls plus a huge fireplace. The garden includes a children's play area. The pub caters equally for drinkers and diners, who are offered an interesting range of dishes including vegetarian and Polish specialities. Bottled local cider available. Closed Mondays in winter. Live music monthly on Fridays.

🏠 Q ❀ ◑ ⅃ 🚍 ♣ 🍴 P ✂

EARDISLAND — C3

Cross Inn

HR6 9BW   In village
☎ (01544) 388249
12-11.30; 11-1am Sat; 12-11 Sun

Fullers London Pride; Greene King Abbot; guest beer

Once a drovers inn, then a coaching inn, and now a friendly village pub, which is open all day and full of local characters. The name probably derives from the nearby river crossing - not the war memorial outside. The pub has a long public bar, a beamed lounge and a restaurant in what used to be the cellars. The garden has an interesting old AA box, and the car park is very small, but the village car park is next door. The food is mainly traditional English.

Q ❀ ⌂ ◑ ⅃ ⅙ 🚍 P ✂

White Swan

HR6 9BD   In village
☎ (01544) 388533
www.whiteswan-eardisland.co.uk
11-11; 12-10.30 Sun

Banks's Original; guest beer

This unspoilt inn looks to be about 200 years old, but to the rear is the timber-framework of a 17th century building. Kept warm and cosy by three real fires, it is divided into a public bar, lounge bar and restaurant area. The family friendly pub caters for all round trade; hosts quoits and two darts teams, and is headquarters of local cricket team. Traditional home-made pub food is served with roasts on Sundays. Live music on alternate Saturdays.

🏠 ❀ ◑ ⅃ ⅃ 🚍 ♣ P ✂

EARDISLEY — B4

New Strand

HR3 6PW   On A4111, in village
☎ (01544) 327285
11 (5 Tue)-11; 12-10.30 Sun

Wood Parish; Wye Valley Butty Bach, Weston's Organic Cider (summer)

Rebuilt in Victorian mock Gothic style after the original pub burnt down in 1900, and now consisting of a single bar, with a cafe/restaurant (doubling as family room), post office and bookshop in the same building. This is a example of how village pubs can diversify to thrive. Known locally as the 'New Inn', it offers a family atmosphere and welcomes cyclists and walkers. A varied food menu is available all day.

🏠 ❀ ◑ ⅃ ⅙ 🚍 ♣ 🍴 P ✂

Tram Inn

HR3 6PG   On A4111, in village
☎ (01544) 327251
12-2.30; 6-11; 12-2.30, 7-10.30 Sun

Greene King IPA; Taylor Landlord; guest beer

The name of this black and white inn refers to the Kington Railway, a horse-operated plateway that passed nearby until 1874, from which a preserved plate section is on view. The much altered 17th century building has a public bar and a lounge with exposed beams and cosy corners. Eardisley is on the Black and White Village Trail.

🏠 Q ❀ ◑ ⅃ ⅃ 🚍 ♣ P

WESTONS CIDER
— ESTD 1880 —
VISITORS CENTRE

Visit the Home of Traditional Cider Making in Herefordshire

Take a tour of the Cider Mill to experience the living history of over 125 years of traditional cider making.
Tours daily at 11.00am & 2.30pm

H Weston & Sons Ltd
The Bounds, Much Marcle, Ledbury, Herefordshire HR8 2NQ
Tel: 01531 660108
www.westons-cider.co.uk

EWYAS HAROLD — C7

Dog Inn

HR2 0EX Just off B4347, in village
☎ (01981) 240598
www.thedoginn.net
10-midnight; 10-1 Fri,Sat; 10-11 Sun
Brains Rev James; guest beer

Name changing is not a new phenomenon - since 1509 this stone-built village inn has been the Bell, Dog, Castle and Dog again! Consisting of a main bar plus games room and restaurant, its beers are drawn from local and regional breweries and draught Gwatkins cider is occasionally available. Home-prepared and locally-sourced meals are served in the restaurant, and at lunchtimes also as bar snacks. Live music features, typically monthly, and a beer festival is held from time to time.

Temple Bar

HR2 0EU Just off B4347, in village
☎ (01981) 240423
12-midnight;12-2am Fri, Sat; 12-11.30 Sun
Beer range varies

A large 200 year old stone built village centre pub, whose name derives from its role as a courthouse in the 18/19th century. The small lounge and two restaurants are in the oldest part of the building. The Victorian stables have been converted to provide the large main bar. Food ranges from bar snacks to full à la carte including a children's menu (not served Sun eve and Mon). Will have changed licensee by the time this guide is published.

FORD BRIDGE — D3

Hickory Stick

Grove Golf Centre, HR6 0LE Just E of A49
OS 512552
☎ (01568) 610602
www.grovegolf.co.uk
11-8; 12-8 Sun
Woods Parish Bitter

This clubhouse, restaurant and bar is in a modern building on a golf course and driving range. The single bar, with gallery seating, offers fine views across the range and countryside beyond. There are no membership restrictions and both diners and drinkers are served, including families. The snack and à la carte menus use locally-sourced ingredients. Evening closing time may be later if required. Full disabled facilities available.

FOWNHOPE — E6

Green Man

HR1 4PE On B4224, in village
☎ (01432) 860243
11-11; 11-midnight Fri, Sat; 11-11 Sun
Courage Directors; Fullers London Pride

Claimed to date from 1485, and formerly called the Naked Boy, this ancient inn abounds with historical connections - including the Civil War, magistrates' courts, and Tom Spring the prize-fighter. Although the building has been much altered, both internally and externally, it manages to look genuinely old. There is one main bar, a small lounge area, a pool room and a restaurant. Traditional pub food is served all day, with a carvery Sunday lunctime.

New Inn

HR1 4PE On B4224, in village
☎ (01432) 860350
12-2, 6-11; 11-11 Sat; 12-3, 7-10.30 Sun
Hobsons Best Bitter; Tetley Bitter; Woods Shropshire Lad

Contrasting with its older neighbour, this is mainly a locals' pub. There are two areas, one in public bar style and the other in lounge bar style, served from a single bar where you are quite likely to get caught up in the friendly banter. Fownhope football team use the pub as a base. Traditional pub food is served Mon-Fri lunchtimes with a blackboard menu.

※ (ᕦ 🚲 ♣ P

Garway Moon
Garway Common, HR2 8RQ OS 465227
☎ (01600) 750270
12-3, 7-12; 12-midnight Sat, Sun
Beer range varies

A remote, but popular, welcoming pub overlooking the delightful village green and cricket pitch, with lounge and public bar plus a separate snug/family room and garden. Beers are from regional and local breweries. Traditional, good value home-prepared bar and restaurant meals are served.

🚲 ⛄ ※ ⇆ (ᕦ Å ♣ P

Cross Keys
HR9 6JB Just SE of A40 OS 567190
☎ (01600) 891168
9-11 daily
Courage Directors; Youngs Special: Bulmers Traditional; Black Rat cider

This friendly and enthusiastically run, two-bar village inn, just off the Goodrich Cross exit of the A40, was once a coaching inn (a mounting block remains in place at the front). The public bar has a games area, whilst the small lounge leads to an interesting barn-style restaurant. To the rear is a skittle alley and an outdoor play area. An enterprising menu of freshly prepared bar snacks and full meals is starting to win a reputation locally under recent new ownership.

🚲 ※ (ᐅ 🚲 ♣ 🍴 P

Hostelrie Hotel
HR9 6HX 1 mile SW of A40, in village
OS 575194
☎ (01600) 890241
www.ye-hostelrie.co.uk
11-1am; 11-11.30 Sun
Draught Bass; Wye Valley Bitter; guest beer: Westons cider

Ye Hostelrie is an early Victorian conversion of the old Crown and Anchor pub, in a romantic Gothic style reflecting the design of Goodrich Court, now demolished. In a village of great

historical interest, it now caters for hotel guests, diners and drinkers. A single bar area opens into a no-smoking lounge and there is a separate hotel-style restaurant. Food ranges from traditional homemade bar snacks to full restaurant meals. Westons 1st Quality or Old Rosie cider alternate with Perry.

※ ⇆ (ᐅ Å 🚲 ♣ 🍴 P ✄

Roadmaker
HR9 7SW On B4221, at W end of village
☎ (01989) 720352
12-3, 4.30-11; 12-11 Sat; 12-10.30 Sun
Brains Reverend James; Butcombe Best Bitter

The result of a competition to find a new name for the New Inn, recalled a lengthman who used to break roadstone on the site. The large, comfortable bar, with a pool table at one end, has beamed ceilings and is decorated with nautical paraphernalia, whilst the restaurant is a modern extension with a bar in the shape of a boat. Steakhouse-style food is served, using local beef with a carvery at weekends, for which it is advisable to book.

🚲 ※ (ᐅ ᕦ Å 🚲 P ✄

Grafton Inn
HR2 8ED On A49
☎ (01432) 355233
12-3, 6-11; 12-3, 7-10.30 Sun
Rhymney Bitter; Wye Valley Butty Bach; guest beer

This roadside pub has benefitted from a very smart and tasteful refurbishment. Whilst clearly aimed at the dining market, it includes a public bar with pool table. A restaurant, conservatory and children's play area complete the layout, whilst outside is a large pond and (separate) children's play area. Bar snacks at lunchtime give way to an extensive and varied menu and specials in the evening. Full disabled facilities.

※ (ᐅ 🗗 ᕦ 🚲 ♣ P

Major's Arms
WR6 5AX E of B4124 OS 675481
☎ (01531) 640371

Unassuming single-bar pub that enjoys stunning views across the Frome Valley. Once temporarily renamed the Miners Arms during the pit closure furore in the early 1990's this pub is currently closed, and its future is uncertain.

HAMPTON BISHOP   E5

Bunch of Carrots
HR1 4JR On B4224
☎ (01432) 870237
11-3, 6-11; 11-11 Fri, Sat; 12-10.30 Sun
Butcombe Bitter; Courage Directors; Spinning Dog Organic

Situated on the banks of the River Wye - this is a much extended pub, parts of which date back to the 17th century. Much timber is visible, dividing the pub into drinking and eating areas, together with some bare walls and a flagstone floor. Home prepared food is important here, the pub catering strongly for out-of-town diners, although not to the exclusion of drinkers. The menu is quite varied and includes a carvery. Full facilities for disabled customers.

HAREWOOD END   E7

Harewood End Inn
HR2 8JT On A49
☎ (01989) 730637
12-3, 6-11 (midnight Fri,Sat); 12-3,7-10.30 Sun
Beer range varies (1 winter, 2 summer)

A very old roadside pub, which in coaching days provided horses for the climb to Hereford, and later housed a magistrates court. Recently refurbished, the compact and cosy bar with wood burner leads out to a beer garden and to two separate eating areas - the smaller panelled and with an open fire. An interesting menu of freshly-prepared food is offered and booking is advised at weekends. Beers are from regional or local breweries. Families welcome.

HEREFORD   D5

Bar Spirit
32 Union Street, HR1 2BT
☎ (01432) 342101
No real ale or cider

Built early in the twentieth century as the New Harp on the site of an earlier pub of the same name. Name changes frequently.

Barrels
69 St Owen Street, HR1 2JQ
☎ (01432) 274968
11-11.30(midnight Fri,Sat); 11-11.30 Sun
Wye Valley Bitter, Hereford Pale Ale, Butty Bach, Dorothy Goodbody's Wholesome Stout , seasonal beers: Thatchers Traditional cider

Once home to Wye Valley Brewery and is still the brewery's flagship outlet - stocking most of the beer range. Voted Herefordshire Pub of the Year 2003, it is one of the city's few remaining multi-roomed pubs: its four distinct rooms catering for all age groups. A pool table occupies one bar, and another has a large-screen TV (only used for major sporting events). Conversation rules unless there is live music, and it can get busy on weekend evenings. Freed from brewery activities, the rear courtyard now provides a great outdoor drinking area complete with new decking and patio heaters, and is the venue for the August Bank Holiday charity music and beer festival. A skittle alley doubles as a meeting room.

HEREFORD

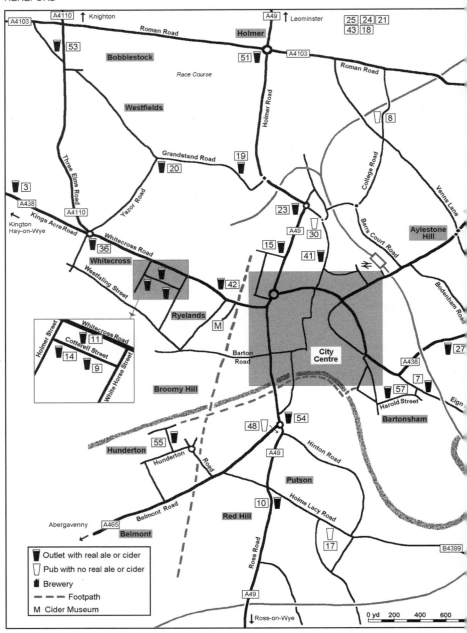

Page 36

HEREFORD

Hereford City Pubs

1	Bar Spirit	21	Grapes Tavern	41	Oxford Arms
2	Barrels	22	Green Dragon Hotel	42	Plough
3	Bay Horse	23	Heart of Oak	43	Queens Arms
4	Black Lion	24	Herdsman	44	Rose & Crown
5	Booth Hall	25	Hop Pole	45	Salmon
6	Bowling Green	26	Horse & Groom	46	Saracen's Head
7	Brewer's Arms	27	Hum-ming Garden	47	Saxtys
8	Bridge	28	Imperial	48	Ship
9	Britannia	29	J Ds	49	Spread Eagle
10	Broadleys	30	Karlo's	50	Stagecoach
11	Buckingham	31	Kerry	51	Starting Gate
12	Cock of Tupsley	32	Kings Fee	52	Swan
13	Commercial	33	Lichfield Vaults	53	Three Elms
14	Cotterell Arms	34	Litten Tree	54	Treacle Mine
15	Courtyard	35	Merton Hotel (Bar 28)	55	Vaga Tavern
16	Exchange	36	Monument	56	Victory
17	Game Cock	37	Moorfield	57	Volunteer
18	Golden Fleece	38	Nell Gwynne	58	Watercress Harry's
19	Golden Lion	39	Newmarket	59	Whitehouse
20	Grandstand	40	Orange Tree	60	(Beer on the Wye)

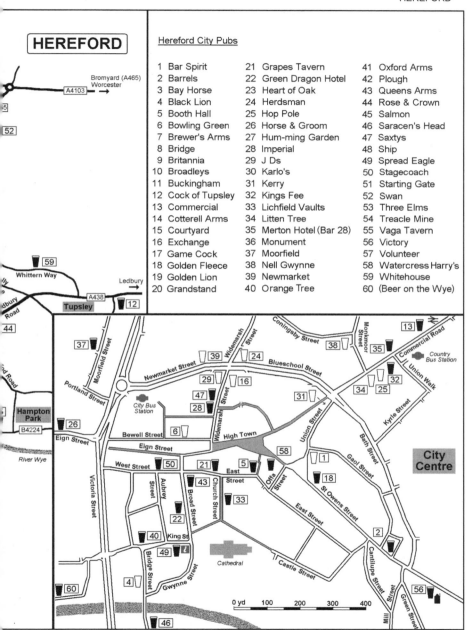

Bay Horse
236 King's Acre Road, HR4 0SD
☎ (01432) 273351
www.thebayhorsehereford.co.uk
12-3, 5.30-11.30; 12-4, 6-10.30 Sun
Fullers London Pride; Greene King Abbot

A small 19th century roadside inn, that has been much modernised and extended at the front to give a large bar with a smaller non-smoking area together with a more recent conservatory. An accommodation block is being added. Now primarily an eating house, this busy pub still caters for a small group of locals. Children allowed.

Q ✿◑▶ 告 🚌 P ⚞

Black Lion
31 Bridge Street, HR4 9DG
☎ (01432) 354016
www.hereford.co.uk/blacklion
12-midnight (2am Sat, Sun) (no entry after 11pm)
Greene King Old Speckled Hen; Wye Valley Bitter

This historic, sixteenth century inn, although substantially altered over the years has recently been sympathetically refurbished. The large single bar is divided into several areas and, although predominantly an eating house at lunchtime, there is still plenty of room for drinkers. It also has a function room and skittle alley. Traditional English food is served. Entertainment at weekends.

🛏 ✿◑ 告 🚌 ♣ P

Booth Hall
East Street, HR1 2LW
☎ (01432) 344487
11-11; 7-10.30 Sun
Boddingtons Bitter;Tetley Bitter

A historic house, near the town centre, where those convicted of minor offences had the privilege of being detained rather than in the county gaol. Use as licensed premises probably dates from the late 17th century. The oldest part of the building, dating from the fourteenth century and partly above the Booth Hall Passage has been revealed by a recent very modern style refurbishment. Now caters for a mainly young clientele, with a heated patio outside and pool table. Food is toasted baguettes and light 'modern' pub fare.

✿◑ 告 ⇌ 🚌

Bowling Green
Bewell Street, HR4 0BA
☎ (01432) 279213
No real ale or cider

Twentieth century replacement for an older pub, aligned to a new, wide road that was never built.

Brewer's Arms
97 Eign Road, HR1 2RU
☎ (01432) 273746
12-11 daily
Thatchers Heritage cider

Small locals' two-bar pub with games room at the rear with skittle alley, pool table and large screen TV. Angling is featured - the pub is used by local anglers for weighing in.

🛏 ✿⬚ 🚌 ♣ ●

Bridge
College Road, HR1 1JR
☎ (01432) 356679
No real ale or cider

Long established, modern estate style pub on northern edge of city.

Britannia
7 Cotterell Street, HR4 0HH
☎ (01432) 272908
12-midnight; 12-10.30 Sun
Worthington Bitter

A single-bar back street terraced pub, one of two rare survivors in the same street. This is a true community pub in which the open plan bar is complemented by a pool room which doubles as a family room. The secure beer garden has a children's play area. Good value traditional pub snacks and meals are served until early evening, and later by pre-arrangement. Live music Monthly on Saturdays.

🏠 🍴 ⚙ 🍺 ♿ 🚌 ♣

Broadleys
93 Ross Road, HR2 7RP
☎ (01432) 273245

No real ale or cider

Large 1930s roadside pub built in a then rapidly expanding part of the city.

Buckingham
141 Whitecross Road, HR4 0LS
☎ (01432) 276087

5.30-11; 12-midnight Sat; 12-11 Sun Single changing beer

Friendly, two-bar locals' pub on main road to the west, dating from the mid nineteenth century. The public bar has a pool table; the hand-pumps are only in the lounge. Outside is a skittle alley and two beer gardens. Disabled toilet facilities are available.

Q ⚙ 🍴 ♿ 🚌 ♣ P

Cock of Tupsley
Hampton Dene Road, HR1 1UX
☎ (01432) 274911

11.30-11; 11-30-11.30 Fri, Sat; 11.30-11 Sun

Banks's Original, Bitter

Large pub, built in 1968 on the edge of the city, consisting of a public bar with pool table, quoits, darts, and large screen TV, plus an airy and spacious lounge. A varied, traditional pub menu is available (not Sun eve) with '2 for 1' offers generally available. Full disabled facilities are available and there is a large outdoor children's play area.

🍴 ⚙ 🍺 🍽 ♿ 🚌 ♣ P ✗

Commercial
44 Commercial Road, HR1 2BG
☎ (01432) 272379

12-3, 7-12; 12-3, 7-1am Fri, Sat; 12-3, 7-10.30 Sun

Banks's Bitter, Original (winter only)

A Victorian hotel very near the railway and country bus stations with a flamboyant but unspoilt frontage. The two-bar interior is similarly unspoilt, with an excellent gantry prominent in the public bar. Some of its earlier customers are captured in the autobiographical stories of local playwright Alick Rowe entitled 'Boy at the Commercial'. A good local following in a traditional pub. No admission after 11pm.

🏠 ⚙ 🍺 🍴 🚂 🚌 ♣

Cotterell Arms
65-67 Cotterell Street, HR4 0HH
☎ (01432) 266036

6-11; 6-midnight Fri; 11-midnight Sat; 12-10.30 Sun

Hancocks Bitter

This two-bar, back street community pub caters for locals and the members of the sixteen pub-game teams which it supports. One of two rare survivors in the same street, it was formed from an end-of-terrace house in the nineteenth century. It now features a new skittle alley, which will also be used for live music and other events.

🍴 ♿ 🚌 ♣

Courtyard
Edgar Street, HR4 9JR
☎ (01432) 359252
www.courtyard.org.uk
10-11; normally closed Sun

Single changing beer

Popular and lively new Centre for the Arts with very modern exterior and more traditionally styled auditorium; an all non-smoking venue. Beer is from Wye Valley, and an interesting selection of food is served. Real ale may not be available at times of low demand. Full disabled facilities. Car Park is pay and display.

⚙ 🍺 ♿ 🚂 🚌 P ✗

Exchange
40 Widemarsh Street, HR4 9EP
☎ (01432) 276709
No real ale or cider
A new pub in an old building.

Game Cock
38 Holme Lacy Road, HR2 6BY
☎ (01432) 274850
No real ale or cider
1930s main road pub

Golden Fleece
1 St Owen Street, HR1 2JB
☎ (01432) 344398
10-11; 12-10.30 Sun
Banks's Original, Bitter

City centre pub rebuilt after a fire in the late eighteenth century and once alleged to have been illicitly supplying the nearby County Gaol with liquor via a rear window. It consists of a single long narrow panelled bar.

≷ 🍺

Golden Lion
36 Grandstand Road, HR4 9NF
☎ (01432) 275785
10-11; 10-10.30 Sun
Thatchers Traditional Cider

Friendly two-bar locals' free house, once a pair of cottages. The large public bar has original etched windows and is decorated with a tapestry and pictures of lions, plus a collection of plates. Behind the public bar is an aviary, complete with a fishpool, which functions as a family area, and a skittle alley. Lunch is served Sunday only.

Q ☎ ⊛ ◁ 🍺 ⅋ 🍺 ✢ ● P ⚡

Grandstand
Grandstand Road, HR4 9NH
☎ (01432) 370867
www.hungryhorse.co.uk
12-11; 12-midnight Fri, Sat; 12-11 Sun
Greene King Abbot

Modern estate pub thoroughly refurbished as a 'Hungry Horse' which specialises in large, good-value meals, predominantly grills, although lesser appetites are also catered for. The open

plan space is divided into over-18s bar, with pool table, lounge and family lounge (with eating facilities throughout). A disabled toilet and baby change room is provided. Live music once each month.

⊛ ◁ ▷ 🍺 ⅋ 🍺 ✢ P ⚡

Grapes Tavern
East Street, HR1 2LW
☎ (01432) 263343
No real ale or cider

Historic pub dating from early 19th Century, but containing parts of an earlier building. Sensitively restored in the early 1990s.

Green Dragon Hotel
44-46 Broad Street, HR4 9BG
☎ (01432) 272506
www.greendragon-hereford.co.uk
11-1am; 11-11 Sun
Wye Valley Bitter; Butty Bach

Although having grown progressively over several centuries, this large and imposing hotel looks like a single building due to its classical façade. Its bar serves real ale and light meals, and the hotel lounge and restaurant are open to non-residents. Limited car park for residents. Disabled facilities.

🛏 ◁ ▷ ⚿ ≷ 🍺 P

Heart of Oak
47 Newtown Road, HR4 9LJ
☎ (01432) 360858
12-11; 12-midnight Fri, Sat; 12-11 Sun
Brains Bitter, Reverend James, house beer

A pub that has grown by absorbing an adjoining shop, and which has been opened out by successive refurbishments. It now consists of a single central bar serving split level areas, furnished variously with sofas, tables and chairs, and benches. Sport is shown on large screen TVs, and a pool table is provided. Meals are served all day except Sun eves. Quiz night Tuesday; karaoke Sunday. Wheelchair toilet.

⊛ 🛏 ◁ ▷ ⚿ 🍺 ✢ P ⚡

Herdsman
54 Widemarsh Street, HR4 9HG
☎ (01432) 277330

No real ale or cider

Old commercial hotel, just outside the ring road.

Hop Pole
Commercial Road, HR1 2BP
☎ (01432) 355674
11-11; 11-midnight Fri, Sat; 12-10.30 Sun
Wye Valley Bitter, Butty Bach

An eighteenth century coaching inn, which fell victim to the Irish theme pub vogue in the mid 1990s, and has now returned to its roots and its old name. A spacious bar leads round to a 'bottle bar' furnished with sofas, and on to an elevated games area with two pool tables. The whole area has bare, polished floorboards. Traditional bar meals are served lunchtime and early evening (not Sun). Other Wye Valley beers may substitute.

Q ❀ ◑ ▶ ♿ ⇌ 🍺 ♣ P

Horse & Groom
140 Eign Street, HR4 0AP
☎ (01432) 355026
No real ale or cider

A pub that once had extensive stables for visitors arriving in the city from the west.

Hum-ming Garden
2 Foley Street, HR1 2SG
☎ (01432) 275642
5.30-11.30 Tue-Thu; 5.30-midnight Fri-Sat; 12-3, 5.30-11.30 Sun
Flowers Original; Wye Valley Bitter

Previously a pub called the Moss Cottage, now a Chinese Restaurant with real ale. Non-diners are served, but the tiny bar can get very crowded in the early evening. Cantonese and Pekingese cuisine with buffet only on Tues eve and Sunday lunchtime. Take away service available. An ideal place to go for a drink with a Chinese meal.

❀ ◑ ▶ ♿ 🍺 P

Imperial
Widemarsh Street, HR4 9EA
☎ (01432) 360931
11-11; 12-10.30 Sun
Wye Valley Bitter, house beer

Built at the beginning of the twentieth century, but looking much older on the outside, the Imperial is newly refitted in contemporary open-plan style. A separate area to the rear has a large screen for sports TV and there is a large decked area outside, and function room upstairs. Used by shoppers at lunchtime, it is mainly a young people's pub in the evenings. A mix of traditional and modern pub fare is available all day. House beer is from Wye Valley.

❀ ◑ ▶ ♿ 🍺

J Ds
57 Widemarsh Street, HR4 9EA
☎ (01432) 272886
No real ale or cider

A survivor of the 1967 ring road which caused the demise of so many pubs in this area, it has succumbed to a name change and complete change of style.

Karlo`s
Widemarsh Street, HR4 9HE
☎ (01432) 266255
No real ale or cider

Large suburban pub, built as the Racehorse in 1939. Now a sports and games pub specialising in pool.

Kerry
Commercial Street, HR1 2DJ
☎ (01432) 266622
No real ale or cider

Built in the mid nineteenth Century, the Kerry Arms was named after the founder of local almshouses. Was briefly the non-brewing Farmhand & Firkin before another name change in 1999.

Kings Fee
49-53 Commercial Road, HR1 2BJ
☎ (01432) 373240
9-midnight daily
Greene King Abbot Ale; Marston Pedigree Bitter; guest beers (5); Westons Old Rosie cider

J D Wetherspoon conversion of an old supermarket, highly commended in the 2004 CAMRA National Pub Design Awards. The large open-plan main bar leads to an elevated family area (children welcome up to 5.00pm), and a courtyard. Decor is contemporary in style, and features local history panels and woodcut prints by a local artist. It has brought to Hereford a welcome choice of guest ales at reasonable prices. Good value food is served all day. Non-smoking throughout.

Q ☎ ⊛ ◑ ▶ ♿ ≈ 🚌 🍺 ⊬

Lichfield Vaults
11 Church Street, HR1 2LR
☎ (01432) 267994
11-11; 12-11 Sun
Greene King Abbot; Marstons Pedigree; Theakstons Best Bitter; Wells Bombardier: guest beer
Westons First Quality cider

An eighteenth century pub hidden away in a charming cobbled alley leading from High Town to the Cathedral. Although opened out to a single bar, modernisation has been fairly subdued, and it retains an intimate feel. Guest beers are drawn mainly from regionals and larger micros. With meals and snacks available at lunchtimes, it is popular with office workers and shoppers. It can get crowded weekend evenings. Recently extended beer garden.

⊛ ◑ ♿ 🚌 ♣

Litten Tree
58 Commercial Road, HR1 2BP
☎ (01432) 273078
No real ale or cider

Modern development in old warehouse.

Merton Hotel (Bar 28)
28 Commercial Road, HR1 2BD
☎ (01432) 265925
www.themertonhotel.co.uk
11-11; 12-11 Sun
Wye Valley Bitter; guest beer

Comfortable and popular hotel bar and lounge near railway station, country bus station and cinema. Varied homemade bar menu plus full à la carte menu in the restaurant.

Q ⊛ 🛏 ◑ ▶ ≈ 🚌 P

Monument
Whitecross Road, HR4 0LT
☎ (01432) 273180
11-11; 11-midnight Fri, Sat; 11-11 Sun
Greene King Abbot

Built in 1961 by Rhymney Brewery and recently refurbished by Greene King in contemporary style, this is a large single bar pub with plenty of TV screens showing sport and three pool tables. The handpumps are steel, to match the other bar fittings. Modern pub food is served - all day at weekends. Quiz on Sunday evening

⊛ ◑ ▶ ♿ ♣ P ⊬

Moorfield Inn
33 Moorfield Stree, HR4 9JL
☎ (01432) 263082
No real ale or cider

End of terrace, back street one-bar pub.

Nell Gwynne
9-11 Monkmoor Street, HR1 2DX
☎ (01432) 354393
No real ale or cider

Mid nineteenth century back-street inn, until fairly recently called the British Oak.

Newmarket
Newmarket Street, HR4 9HR
☎ (01432) 278993
No real ale or cider

An early nineteenth century house adapted, in the middle of the century as a pub to serve the livestock market.

Orange Tree
16 King Stree, HR4 9BX
☎ (01432) 267698
11-11.30; 11-12.30am Fri, Sat; 12-11 Sun
Greene King Old Speckled Hen; Shepherd Neame Spitfire; guest beer

Probably dating from the seventeenth century, this single-bar pub has been much altered, and recently refurbished following a fire. It caters for shoppers and office workers at lunchtimes and younger people in the evening. The menu is mainly traditional pub fare. Full disabled facilities.

⊛ ◑ ▶ ♿ ≈ 🚌 ⊬

Oxford Arms
111 Widemarsh Street, HR4 9EZ
☎ (01432) 272635
11-11; 12-10.30 Sun

Draught Bass: Addlestones Cider

Very welcoming seventeenth century timber-framed building which, although much altered over the years, still retains much character. This small, two-bar pub has a separate pool room and a large garden. It enjoys a loyal community following, with live music some Saturday evenings. Basket meals and filled rolls are available. Convenient for the football ground, with a large public car park to the rear.

🏨 ⌘ ◖◗ ⬚ ⇌ 🚌 ♣ 🍴

Plough Inn
86 Whitecross Road, HR4 0DH
☎ (01432) 273868
12-midnight daily
Greene King IPA, Abbot

A 1930s mock half-timbered replacement for a sixteenth century pub of the same name. There are two basic bars, a skittle alley and a secluded beer garden. Live music is featured every Saturday. Very small car park.

⌘ ⬚ 🚌 ♣ P

Queens Arms
4-5 Broad Street, HR4 9AP
☎ (01432) 273015
10-11; 10-midnight Fri, Sat; 12-midnight Sun
Flowers Original; Wye Valley Bitter

Behind the Victorian frontage lies a small timber-framed building that was once a separate pub, the Punchbowl. Now joined up, and also incorporating an old newsagents on the south side, this pub has bare-boarded floors, timber beams and a preserved section of wattle and daub wall. It consists of the main bar, a TV room and a dart room. It serves as a friendly community meeting place. Lunches served Wed - Fri, Sun only. Live music Sat eve and Sun afternoon. No admission after 11pm.

◖◗ & ⇌ 🚌 ♣

Rose & Crown
152 Ledbury Road, HR1 1RG
☎ (01432) 273272
11.30-11; 12-10.30 Sun
Greene King Ruddles County, Abbot

This recently refurbished 1930s main road pub has a large lounge with separate no-smoking area. The separate public bar is described as a

sports bar, having large screen TVs, and two pool tables. Food is available all day, offering generous 'Giant Menu' portions, Sunday roasts and a children's menu with special offers (Mon-Wed). Full disabled facilities are provided. Greene King seasonal beers sometimes substitute for the Ruddles County.

⌘ ◖◗ ⬚ & ⇌ 🚌 ♣ P ⚲

Salmon Inn
Hampton Park Road, HR1 1TQ
☎ (01432) 272236
11-11; 11-midnight, Fri, Sat; 12-10.30 Sun
Draught Bass; Brains Reverend James

Converted in 1956 from a gentleman's residence to replace the historic Whalebone, the lower storey of which still remains nearby. The Salmon is now a popular, comfortably furnished pub with one large bar extending into a conservatory. Home-prepared, traditional pub food is served (not Sun eve and Mon).

Q ⌘ 🖪 ◖◗ & 🚌 ♣ P ⚲

Saracen's Head Inn
1 St Martin's Street, HR2 7RD
☎ (01432) 275480
12-1am; 12-2am Fri, Sat; 12-1am Sun
Greene King Abbot; guest beer (occasional)

One of Hereford's oldest buildings, the Saracen's Head is situated on the River Wye by the old bridge, which was the only road crossing of the river in the city until 1967. Run by the longest serving publican in the city, the front bar overlooks the river with seating outside, whilst the back bar serves as a pool room, and as a public bar at weekends - both bars would benefit from some redecoration. There is also a function room and skittle alley. Bar snack menu available at lunchtimes. Children welcome.

🍴 Q ☆ ◖◗ ⬜ ♿ 🚌 ♣

Saxtys
33 Widemarsh Street, HR4 9EA
☎ (01432) 357872
www.saxtys.co.uk
10-10; 10-11 Thu; 10-3am Fri, Sat; 8pm-2.30am Sun (Bank Holidays only)
Spinning Dog Hereford Organic Bitter

Town centre bar, restaurant and club, now serving real ale to complement its interesting range of draught and bottled foreign beers. The front bar and restaurant lead through to the library bar, where bookshelves on the wall suggest a previous use of this building. The gallery houses a champagne bar, whilst to the rear is a covered and heated garden. Sandwiches and a wide range of cooked-to-order dishes are on the menu. Families welcome until 6pm. Closed Sundays except bank holidays.

🛏 ◖◗ ♿ ⇌ 🚌 ✗

Ship Inn
6 Ross Road, HR2 7RL
☎ (01432) 272921
No real ale or cider

Enlarged old pub located on a busy roundabout, previously the Plaisterers Arms.

Spread Eagle
2 King Street, HR4 9BW
☎ (01432) 272205
11-11; 11-midnight Thu; 11-2 Fri, Sat; 11-midnight Sun
Draught Bass; Fullers London Pride

This old-established inn, still with its stable entrance, has been refurbished and knocked-through to cater for its dual role - serving business customers and tourists by day, and the student set in the evening. There are two bars downstairs and a restaurant upstairs. Music is important, with a DJ most nights and occasional live bands. The varied menu has traditional and Mediterranean themes and a barbecue is held on summer Sundays.

☆ ◖◗ ♿ ⇌ 🚌 ✗

Stagecoach
45 West Street, HR4 0BX

☎ 07974 480078
10-11; 12-10.30 Sun
Rhymney Bitter; Sharps Doom Bar; Wye Valley Bitter; guest beer: Westons Old Rosie cider

Although much changed from its days as a coaching inn, the former Nelson Inn has much original timber on view, with a dining room upstairs and a comfortably furnished bar downstairs. Traditional pub fare includes a range of home-made bar snacks and full meals, including vegetarian options. Guest beers include the full range of Wye Valley seasonal beers.

🍴 Q ◖◗ ♿ 🚌 ♣ 🍎

Starting Gate
Holmer Road, HR4 9RS
☎ (01432) 274853
10.30-11; 12-10.30 Sun
Banks's Bitter; Draught Bass

This Beefeater and Premier Travel Inn was converted from a private house in the 1950s, with the accommodation block added more recently. There is a large, comfortably furnished bar, and the restaurant is on two floors with an upstairs glasshouse. The all-day food is family orientated. Full disabled facilities. Due for full refurbishment and 'rebranding' in 2006.

☆ 🛏 ◖◗ ♿ 🚌 P

Swan
175 Aylestone Hill, HR1 1JJ
☎ (01432) 275234
11.30-3, 5.30-11; 12-3, 7-10.30 Sun
Banks's Original, Bitter

Taken over by Banks's in the 1990's, the Swan has been extended and thoroughly refurbished. A large central bar serves several comfortably furnished areas, which cater for both diners and drinkers. A varied, good value menu is available, with a carvery Sunday lunchtimes, but no food Sun eves. An attractive beer garden is across a small stream. Full disabled facilities.

Q ☆ ◖◗ ♿ ⇌ 🚌 P ✗

Three Elms
1 Canon Pyon Road, HR4 9QQ
☎ (01432) 273338
11-11; 12-10.30 Sun
Greene King Abbot, Ruddles County; guest beers (2)

Large open-plan pub on the edge of a housing estate near the racecourse. Sporting events, especially football and rugby, are shown on a big screen TV in a corner of the bar. The guest beers may be from regional or micro breweries. Modern pub food - both snacks and main meals, are served. Wheelchair WC.

❀ ◖ 🚻 🚍 ♣ P ⚡

Treacle Mine
85 St Martin's Street, HR2 7RG
☎ (01432) 266022
11-midnight; 11-11 Sun
Brains Bitter

Smartly refurbished single bar pub, popular with sports fans and locals. Games include pool, in an alcove to the rear, and table skittles. Barbecues are held on Saturday afternoons in summer and there is live music every Sunday evening. Wheelchair toilet.

◖ ♿ 🚍 ♣

Vaga Tavern
Vaga Street, HR2 7AT
☎ (01432) 273601
12-11; 11-midnight Sat; 12-11 Sun
Banks's Original, Bitter [P]

A friendly community pub on the Hunderton Estate, which is near the River Wye and accessible from the City Centre via a pleasant riverside walk and cycleway. There are two bars, a skittle alley/function room and a garden which is well equipped for children. The lounge has a variety of pictures including several old photographs of Hereford. Beers served by the only remaining electric pump system in Herefordshire. Live music every Saturday.

❀ ◁ ♿ ♣ P ▽

Victory
88 St Owen Street, HR1 2QD
☎ (01432) 274998
3(11summer)-11(midnight Fri, Sat); 12-10.30 Sun
Spinning Dog Top Dog, Oatmeal Stout, Herefordshire Light Ale, Organic Bitter, Owd Bull; guest beers: Weston's cider, perry; Bridge Hill Farm cider

Home of Hereford's Spinning Dog brewery, the pub serves most of its beers, plus the city's best range of real ciders and perry. The main bar is of timber construction with bare wooden floors,

and the bar servery is in the shape of a galleon. The unusual nautical theme continues through to a large narrow bar and skittle alley to the rear. A key venue for local bands (Saturday/Sunday evenings), it holds mini-beer festivals - usually twice per year. Meals Saturday and Sunday only.

🛏 ♨ ❀ ◖ ◁ ⇄ 🚍 ♣ 🍴 P

Volunteer Inn
21 Harold Street, HR1 2QU
☎ (01432) 276189
11-11; 11-midnight Fri, Sat; 11-11 Sun
Adnams Bitter; Draught Bass; Greene King Abbot

There is always a lively and friendly atmosphere at this contemporary community pub, with two bars, skittle alley and a great little snug. Many of the locals are artists and musicians, who organise events at the pub including a monthly folk session (second Wed). Home-prepared food is served daily.

🛏 Q ❀ ◖ ♣ ⚡

Watercress Harry's
8 St Peters Street, HR1 2LE
☎ (01432) 370998
No real ale or cider

After various themes and names, including the Garrick, this pub has re-opened as what its owners class as a 'young persons' venue'.

Whitehouse
Whittern Way, HR1 1PG
☎ (01432) 275981
3-11.30; 12-midnight Fri, Sat; 12-11 Sun
Tetley's Bitter

This 1960s estate pub, popular with locals, consists of large public bar with pool table and large screen TV plus a large panelled lounge. Ansell's branding is very prominent, although the single real ale now comes from Tetley's.

❀ ◁ ♣

New Harp Inn
HR2 6QH In village   OS 545292
☎ (01432) 840900
www.newharpinn.co.uk
12-11 (midnight-3, 6-11 winter); 12-10.30 Sun
Beer range varies (2): Broome Farm Cider [G]

Completely refurbished to a high standard after a fire, this friendly pub comprises one long bar with a stone floor and light modern decor. Home prepared food includes bar snacks and full à la carte, with a fish night on Tuesday and other food events. Beers come from regional and micro-breweries. Newspapers are always on hand to read, and families are welcome. River walks along the Wye are close at hand.

🛏 ✿ ◑ ▶ 🚻 🛅 🚐 🍺 P

HUNTINGTON   A3

Swan

HR5 3PY In village OS 249536

☎ (01544) 370656

No real ale or cider

Remote and eccentric village pub near the Welsh border. Worth the visit to see the remarkable 'other room' - a museum piece.

KENTCHURCH   C7

Bridge Inn

HR2 0BY On B4347

☎ (01981) 240408

12-3 (not Mon, Tue), 5-11; 12-3, 7-10.30 Sun

Beer range varies (2)

Beautifully situated close to the Welsh border on the banks of the River Monnow, the building probably dates from the 14th century. It comprises a welcoming single front bar plus a restaurant with excellent views and boasts riverside gardens and a petanque piste for those summer days. The freshly prepared food ranges from bar snacks to full à la carte, (not served on Sunday evenings). Guest beers are from regional and local breweries; usually one from Wye Valley. Beer Festivals Spring and August Bank Holidays.

🛏 Q ✿ 🛏 ◑ ▶ 🚻 🛅 ♣ P

KERNE BRIDGE   E8

Inn on the Wye

HR9 5QS On B4234

☎ (01600) 890872

www.innonthewye.co.uk

11-11 (11-3,6-11 winter); 12-10.30 Sun

Wye Valley Bitter; guest beer (summer): Westons Cider (summer)

The original name Castle View Hotel alludes to the lovely views across the River Wye to Goodrich Castle from the terrace of this well-situated hotel. The building itself is a former 18th century coaching inn. The main bar has exposed stone and brickwork and a wooden floor giving it a modern feel, and seating includes leather sofas and there is a second bar and separate restaurant. An interesting and varied menu is offered ranging from snacks to full à la carte, all freshly prepared.

Q ✿ 🛏 ◑ ▶ 🚻 🚐 🍺 P

KILPECK   C6

Red Lion

HR2 9DN In village   OS 446304

This pub is currently closed. Planning permission for conversion to residential use has been refused following a vigorous local campaign, backed by Herefordshire CAMRA.

KIMBOLTON   D2

Stockton Cross

HR6 0HD On A4112, W of village

☎ (01568) 612509

12-3, 7-11 (not Mon eve); 12-3 Sun

Teme Valley This; Wye Valley Butty Bach; guest beer (summer)

This single bar black and white pub dates from the sixteenth century and contains some interesting features. Long and narrow, it has a drinking area at one end of the bar whilst the mainly eating area at the other end includes two cosy alcoves set either side of the large fireplace. The food, including a good vegetarian choice, is mainly sourced locally and freshly prepared - and not to be rushed, but quiet conversation can be enjoyed during the wait.

🛏 ✿ ◑ ▶ P ✂

KINGSLAND   C2

Angel

HR6 9QS On B4360, in village

☎ (01568) 708355
www.theangelinnuk.com
12-2.30 (not Mon except B Hols), 6-11.30; 12-2.30, 7-11.30 Sun

Greene King Abbot; Hook Norton Hooky Best; Taylor Landlord; guest beer

Located opposite the church, this interesting 17th century pub has an exquisite timber-framed interior which now comprises a lounge and a restaurant. The large stone fireplace has helped to bring the award of Herefordshire Real Fire Pub 2002. A panel of the original wattle wall is on display behind the lounge. It has a good reputation for its food, which ranges from bar snacks to full meals - booking is advised. Live entertainment every Friday.

⌂ Q ❀ ◑ ❯ 🚌 ✚ P

Corners Inn

HR6 9RY On B4360, in village
☎ (01568) 708385
www.cornersinn.co.uk
11-3, 6-11; 12-3, 7-10.30 Sun

Hobsons Best Bitter; guest beer

A traditional 16th century black and white village inn with a large open-plan bar and a restaurant, with exposed beams in the oldest part of the building. The guest beer is from local breweries. A full range of food from bar snacks to restaurant meals is available and booking is recommended, especially for the Sunday carvery.

⌂ Q ❀ 🛏 ◑ ❯ 🖥 🚌 ✚ P

Bull Ring

HR2 9HE On B4348, in village
☎ (01981) 251834

11.30-3 (not Mon), 6-11; 12-11 Sat,Sun

Greened King IPA; Wye Valley Butty Bach; guest beer

A two-bar pub on a crossroads in the centre of the village. There is a small public bar with pool room to one side, and a large separate restaurant. Note the Alton Court Brewery initials in stained glass in the front porch. The guest beer, from regional or local brewers, changes from time to time. The home-prepared food, not served Sun eve, ranges from lunchtime snacks to full restaurant meals and includes a children's menu. Modernised facilities include a wheelchair toilet.

⌂ Q ❀ ◑ 🖥 ♿ 🚌 ✚ P

Burton Hotel

Mill Street, HR5 3BQ
☎ (01544) 230323
www.burtonhotel.co.uk
11-11 daily

Greene King Abbot; Wye Valley Bitter; guest beer

An attractive and very traditional former coaching inn with a large main bar, cosy ramblers bar and separate restaurant. Varied bar meals available and salad buffet in summer, plus an à la carte menu in the restaurant. Health and leisure club with swimming pool adjoining. Guest beer usually from Wye Valley.

⌂ Q 🛏 ❀ 🛏 ◑ ♿ 🚌 P

Ewe & Lamb

12 High Street, HR5 3AX
☎ (01544) 239039
12-2.30, 4.30-11; 11-11 Fri-Sun

Draught Bass

High Street locals' pub with bar in single L shaped room. It became the Ewe & Lamb in the early 1990's, but most Kingtonians still use its original name of just 'The Lamb'.

⌂ ◑ ❯ 🚌 ✚

Lion

52 Bridge Street, HR5 3DJ
☎ (01544) 231744

No real ale or cider

Very old pub, now with modern sports bar. Until recently the Talbot, it has reverted approximately to its original name, the Lyon.

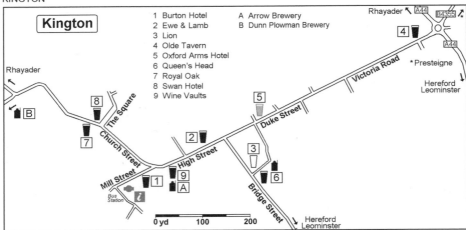

Kington

1 Burton Hotel
2 Ewe & Lamb
3 Lion
4 Olde Tavern
5 Oxford Arms Hotel
6 Queen's Head
7 Royal Oak
8 Swan Hotel
9 Wine Vaults

A Arrow Brewery
B Dunn Plowman Brewery

Olde Tavern
22 Victoria Road, HR5 3BX
☎ (01544) 230122

7- midnight Mon, 6.30-midnight Tue-Thu; 6.30-1 am Fri; 12-3, 6-1am Sat; 12-3, 7-11.30 Sun

Dunn Plowman Tavern Bitter, Shire Horse, Railway Porter, Sting

Once called the House in the Fields, and then the Railway Tavern, this edge-of-town pub mirrors the history of Kington. A real pub for the connoisseur - a two room time warp, voted Herefordshire Pub of the Year in 2004 and Area Pub of the Year in 2005. The main bar is very small and crammed full of interesting curios, along with plans for the 1920 refurbishment that never came to fruition. The tap for the nearby Dunn Plowman Brewery, there is always a warm welcome from staff and locals alike - regulars take an active part in pub games and the Kington festival. The recently opened Jake's Bistro to the rear, has a varied menu (weekends only) using home produced and locally-sourced food – includes Sunday roasts.

Q ❀ ♨ ⛺ ♣

Oxford Arms Hotel
Duke Street, HR5 3DR

Once the main coaching inn for Kington. Temporarily closed.

Queen's Head
50 Bridge Street, HR5 3DW
☎ 07767 891336

3-11; 1-11 Thu-Sun

Dunn Plowman Brewhouse Bitter: Ralph's Badlands Cider

Refurbishment in recent times has enhanced this two bar town pub - particularly highlighting many traditional features. The rounded window and wood floor in the public bar are of particular merit. The lounge offers a quieter environment. Live music 3 or 4 nights per week - acoustic/trad. Buildings to the rear were home to the Dunn Plowman Brewery and, since 2003 the Bridge Street Brewery, but brewing has ceased and the brewhouse is now being converted for residential use.

⛺ ❀ ♨ ⛲ ⛩ ♣ ♠ P

Royal Oak
24 Church Street, HR5 3BE
☎ (01544) 230484

11-2.30 (not Mon), 5.30-1(5-2 Fri,Sat); 12-2.30, 6-midnight Sun

Banks's Bitter, Riding Bitter; guest beer (summer)

A basic, traditional two roomed pub dating from the 17th century although much altered since. It describes itself as the first and last pub in England - a point less significant now that Welsh pubs open on Sundays. An extensive bar menu is available together with roasts on Sundays (food not served Tue or Sun eves).

⛺ Q ❀ ♨ ◑▶ ⛲ ⛩ ♣ ▽

Swan Hotel
Church Street, HR5 3AZ
☎ (01544) 230510

12-midnight, 12-11.30 Sun

Beer range varies

A 17th century hotel with a one room bar divided into areas by a chimney breast. One area has chairs for bar meals and the other has a pool table. There is also a separate restaurant area. Previously known as the Upper Swan to distinguish it from another (Lower) Swan in the High Street. Occasional live music at weekends. Beers are drawn from Spinning Dog, Woods and Wye Valley.

✿🍴 ◖❱ 🚌 ♣ P ✄

Wine Vaults

37 High Street, HR5 3BJ

☎ (01544) 230685

5-midnight Mon, Wed; 11-midnight Tue, Thu; 2.30-1am Fri; 11-1am Sat; 12-midnight Sun

Arrow Bitter, Quiver

Back to its original name after a spell as the Old Fogey, this is a small, quaint, no frills one-bar drinkers' pub. The atmosphere is very convivial. Try playing quoits - a local will soon show you how! The Arrow Brewery is located in outbuildings to the rear of the pub. Park in the town centre car parks.

✿ 🚌 ♣

KINNERSLEY   B4

Kinnersley Arms

HR3 6QA   S of A4112   OS 341487

☎ (01544) 327778

12-3; 6-11 (12-11 summer); 12-3, 6-10.30 (12-10.30 summer) Sun

Banks's bitter; guest beer (summer)

Formerly the Station Hotel, built at the same time as the Hereford, Hay & Brecon Railway,

this is a large pub - interestingly divided into bar, games area, separate snug bar, restaurant and function room. The attractive beer garden has a children's play area. Bar snacks and restaurant meals are available (except Sun eve), homemade with locally-sourced ingredients. Daily specials and a children's menu complement the interesting seasonal menu - booking advised at weekends. Disabled toilet available.

♿ ✿ ◖ 🍴 🕭 ♿ ♣ P

LEA   F7

Crown Inn

HR9 7JZ   On A40, near B4222 junction

☎ (01989) 750407

11-11.30; 12-10.30 Sun

Greene King IPA, Abbot; guest beer

A very old roadside pub with parts dating back to the 14th century, and part which was a butcher's shop - hence the Butchers Bar. The main bar has flagstone floors and there is much exposed woodwork throughout the pub. The main bar has games and seating/dining areas and there is also a separate restaurant. Traditional snacks and meals are served.

🛏 ✿ 🍴 ◖❱ Å 🚌 ♣ 🍺 P

LEDBURY   G5

Brewery Inn

Bye Street, HR8 2AG

☎ (01531) 634272

11-11; 12-10.30 Sun

Banks's Original, Bitter; Marston's Bitter; guest beer: Weston's 1st Quality cider [G]

On the right-hand side of what once was the entrance to Ledbury Town station stands the Brewery Inn, a fascinating and largely unspoilt 15th century two-bar town pub with traditional quarry-tiled floors. Bar snacks available Mon - Fri lunchtimes. Limited free parking nearby.

🛏 Q ✿ ◖❱ ♿ ⇌ 🚌 ♣ 🍺

Feathers Hotel

25 High Street, HR8 1DS

☎ (01531) 635266

www.feathers-ledbury.co.uk

11-11; 12-10.30 Sun

Fullers London Pride; guest beer

An elegant black and white Elizabethan coaching inn, one of the flagship hotels for the county. Inside this fine timber-framed building is a function room that was once the town theatre, and hand painted murals in the upstairs corridors. The smart, comfortable, quiet bar is complemented by the extensive bistro-style 'Fuggles Restaurant' and a more formal brasserie, whilst outside is a large walled garden and patio. An interesting and varied menu is offered, with fish a speciality. Wheelchair toilet.

🏨 ♵ ⚲ ✸ ⌱ ◑ ⧖ ⟲ 🚍 P

Full Pitcher

New Street, HR8 2EN On A438/A449 junction
☎ (01531) 632688
12-11(midnight Tue, Thu); 12-1.30am Fri, Sat; 12-midnight Sun

Greene King Abbot; guest beer

A large, friendly and welcoming local on the outskirts of town (near the ring road), where

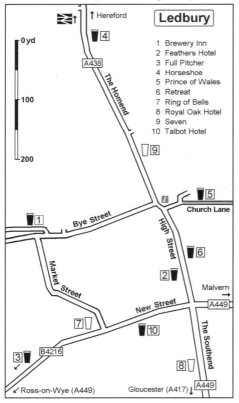

there is an emphasis on pub teams and games. Before acquiring its cricketing name it was called the Biddulph Arms after the family estate to which it belonged. Good value traditional pub meals are served. Full disabled facilities.

⚲ ✸ ◑ ⌱ ⧖ Å 🚍 ♣ P

Horseshoe

The Homend, HR8 1BP
☎ (01531) 632770
11-11.30; 11- midnight Thu; 11- 1am Fri, Sat; 11- 11 Sun

Fullers London Pride; Taylor Landlord; Wye Valley HPA

A large set of stone steps gives access to a long narrow interior with drinking areas front and rear. Many original features have survived a past refurbishment; a cosy feel and some charm add to its character. Families are welcome in the heated patio - up a flight of steps to the rear. Traditional pub food is available at lunchtime and Mon-Wed evenings, with home-prepared roasts on Sunday.

🏨 ✸ ◑ ⌱ ⟲ 🚍 ♣

Prince of Wales

Church Lane, HR8 1DL
☎ (01531) 632250
11-11; 12-10.30 Sun

Banks's Bitter; Brains Reverend James; Sharps Doom Bar; guest beer: Weston's Cider and Perry

Tucked away down a beautiful narrow cobbled street towards the church, this superb friendly 16th-Century timbered pub comprises front and back bars. Always bustling with locals and visitors alike, it holds a very popular folk jam session (Wed eve) and is frequented by a number of pub games teams. It is renowned for offering a wide selection of bottled continental beers. Run with real a verve, excellent value straightforward bar meals and Sunday roasts feature. Parking available in the nearby town car parks. Perry summer only.

⚲ ✸ ◑ ⌱ ⟲ 🚍 ♣ 🍎

Retreat

7 High Street, HR8 1DS
☎ (01531) 632766
12-3 (not Mon), 7-12; 12-midnight Fri, Sat; 3-midnight Sun

Greene King IPA; guest beer

Once the Bulls Head, this is now a stylish single-bar pub with an ornate timber facade. Particularly popular with a younger clientele, it currently offers no food, so the sleekly-furnished modern restaurant to the rear offers a more discrete area to drink, contrasting with the sofas in the front bar area. Food is likely to be reintroduced in the near future. Real ale availability can fluctuate with demand from time to time.

Ring of Bells
27 New Street, HR8 2EA
No real ale or cider

Down-to-earth, no-frills backstreet two-bar pub with an unusual 1970's domestic leanto extension that accommodates a pool room. This pub is changing licensee at the time of printing.

Royal Oak Hotel
The Southend, HR8 2EY
☎ (01531) 632110
No real ale or cider

An old coaching inn, built in 1643 and renovated in 1890, with a new façade covering the original timber-frame. Recently the site of Ledbury Brewery.

Seven
11 The Homend, HR8 1BN
☎ (01531) 631317
No real ale or cider

Successfully emerged from the remains of the fire-ravaged Seven Stars. A sophisticated bistro-restaurant with contemporary decor of an exceptionally high standard contrasts well with the building's many old beams.

Talbot Hotel
14 New Street, HR8 2DX
☎ (01531) 632963
www.visitledbury.co.uk/talbot
11-3, 5-11 (midnight Fri); 11-midnight Sat; 11-4, 7-11 Sun
Wadworth Henry's IPA, 6X; Wye Valley Butty Bach; guest beer

This excellent black-and-white half-timbered hotel dates back to 1596. The heavily-beamed bar surrounds an island servery, offering a range of relaxing and comfortable drinking areas. The beautiful oak-panelled dining room,

with its fine carved overmantel, was once the scene of fighting between Cavaliers and Roundheads. Traditional bar snacks are available and English and Continental dishes are served in the restaurant, all using local ingredients. An ideal place to spend a relaxing short break. Occasional live music. On-street parking available nearby.

LEDGEMOOR   C4

Marshpools Country Inn
Weobley, HR4 8RN To the east of the Weobley - Hereford (via Tillington) road about 1 mile south of Weobley   OS 507419
☎ (01544) 318215
www.country-inn.co.uk
12-3, 7-11 (not Tue); 12-3, 7-10.30 Sun
Banks's Bitter; guest beer

A friendly country inn set in the heart of the Herefordshire countryside near Weobley. The modern building offers a comfortable bar and luxury en-suite accommodation. Outside is an enclosed beer garden and two coarse fishing pools. Reasonably priced, freshly prepared food is available lunchtimes and evenings.

LEINTWARDINE   C1

Lion Hotel
High Street, SY7 0JZ In village, on A4113
☎ (01547) 540203
12-3, 6-11; 12-10.30 Sun
Beer range varies (2)

Fairly large pub/hotel near the river Teme, with lounge, public bar and restaurant. The bars have interesting fireplaces, and there is a pool table in the top bar. The garden overlooks the river in idyllic surroundings. Bar snacks and full menu available, using local produce, with 2-course lunches Monday to Saturday. Real ales from national and regional breweries.

Sun Inn
Rosemary Lane, SY7 9DF

A truly amazing pub, which is in CAMRA's National Inventory of pub interiors. It is an end of terrace cottage with a small entrance hall and, to the right, a drinking parlour furnished with benches and scrubbed wood tables. There is no bar as such - your beer will be fetched from the kitchen. At the time of printing, due to illness of the landlady, the Sun is being operated by a team of neighbours.

♨ Q ⌑ 🚍

LEOMINSTER   D3

Baron's Cross

Baron's Cross Road, HR6 8RS On A44/A4112, at junction with B4529

☎ (01568) 615114

11.30-3; 6-midnight; 11.30-1 Fri-Sun

Hook Norton Hooky Bitter; guest beer (summer)

Rebuilt in the twentieth century in mock half-

timbered style, this large, two-bar roadside pub retains some of its original beams inside. At the front is a large no-smoking lounge, to the rear a public bar with pool table, and to the side a snug. Outside the beer garden has a view across open countryside, and a children's play area. Traditional home-made food is served. Live music monthly on Fridays. The guest beer comes from local breweries. There is no admission after 11pm.

🛏 ⊛ ◑ ⌑ ᪥ 🚍 ♣ P ✂

Bell Inn

☎ **39 Etnam Street, HR6 8AE**

(01568) 612818

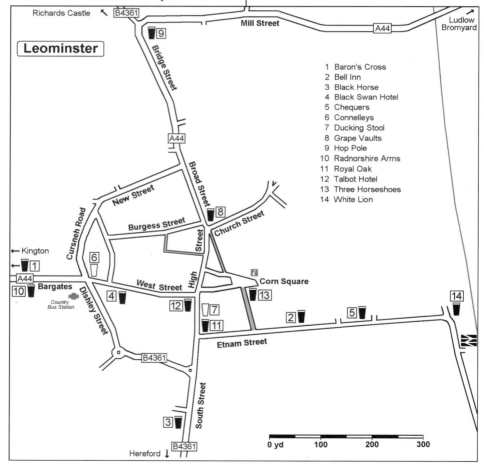

1 Baron's Cross
2 Bell Inn
3 Black Horse
4 Black Swan Hotel
5 Chequers
6 Connelleys
7 Ducking Stool
8 Grape Vaults
9 Hop Pole
10 Radnorshire Arms
11 Royal Oak
12 Talbot Hotel
13 Three Horseshoes
14 White Lion

12-11; 12-10.30 Sun

Wye Valley Bitter; Hobsons Town Crier; guest beers

Herefordshire CAMRA Joint Pub of the Year 2005. A friendly modernised pub with a single island U-shaped bar that provides for a light and airy feel, plus a pleasant garden to the rear. Live music features every Tuesday evening (folk) and Thursday evening (band). On-street parking outside is free and there is a large car park nearby. Reasonably priced, home made pub food is served at lunchtime. Run by a young and enthusiastic licensee who enjoys his beer.

🏚 ✻ ◑ ⇄ 🚌 ♣

Black Horse
74 South Street, HR6 8JF
☎ (01568) 611946
11-2.30, 6-11; 11-11 Sat; 12-3, 7-10.30 Sun
Dunn Plowman BHB; Hobsons Town Crier; guest beers: Addlestones cider

An enthusiastically-run, if somewhat unassuming ex-coach house. One time home to the fledgling Dunn Plowman Brewery, it is still home to an excellent range of beers. It has a traditional public bar; a long, narrow lounge area - resplendent in 1980's decor - and a separate dining area to the rear. Home prepared bar snacks and meals are served (not Sun eve), with Sunday lunches a speciality. Games include petanque, table skittles and quoits. Car park access is via the narrow courtyard entrance.

Q ➷ ✻ ◑ ▯ ⇄ 🚌 ♣ ● P

Black Swan Hotel
33 West Street, HR6 8EP
☎ (01568) 612020
11-11 (midnight Fri, Sat); 12-11 Sun
Hancocks HB: Thatchers Heritage Cider; Westons Country Perry

An 18th century hotel near the town centre with two bars and an eating area. The lounge is plush, whilst the public bar is less so, but quieter. A further drinking area is used for eating at lunchtimes and there is a patio outside. Accommodation is en-suite, bed and breakfast and the food is mainly bar snacks.

➷ ✻ ⇔ ◑ ▯ ⇄ 🚌 ♣ ● ⚥

Chequers
63 Etnam Street, HR6 8AE
☎ (01568) 612473
11-11; 12-10.30 Sun
Banks's Bitter; Wye Valley Butty Bach; guest beer: Westons First Quality Cider

Claiming to be the oldest pub in Leominster, built in 1480, it was once a coaching inn with its own brewery. A superb timber-framed building with protruding gables, it has two contrasting bars. The renovated public bar at the front has a splendid open fire and many charming original features, and there is a quieter lounge bar with eating area to the rear, plus a separate function room. Under keen new ownership, improvements include a new outside patio area.

🏚 Q ◑ ▯ ⇄ 🚌 ♣ ● P

Connelleys
50 West Street, HR6 8EU
No real ale or cider

Was the Bull's Head, now one of the surviving Irish theme bars - but for how long?

Ducking Stool
11 South Street, HR6 8JA
☎ (01568) 614403
No real ale or cider

Young person's pub - was Queen's Head

Grape Vaults
2-4 Broad Street, HR6 8BS
☎ (01568) 611404

11-11; 12-10.30 Sun

Banks's Original, Bitter; Marston Pedigree; guest beers (2)

Herefordshire CAMRA Pub of the Year Runner-up for 2004 and once a 'hard-core' cider house, this is an unadulterated treat. The original wood-panelled single main bar is resplendent with snug, roaring fire and bench seating. Good conversation is guaranteed in this cosy haven - the TV only features during major rugby games. The Gents toilets must be the smallest In England? Conventional English pub food is served (not Sundays) at affordable prices, with local ingredients. One of the guests is from Woods.

🏚 Q ◁🌒 ⇌ 🚌

Hop Pole
Bridge Street, HR6 8QS
☎ (01568) 620504
11-11; 12-4, 7-10.30 Sun
Greene King IPA; guest beer

A much-altered 17th century two-bar pub. The guest beer is from regional or micro-breweries. Food ranges from bar snacks to an à la carte menu plus traditional Sunday lunches, and booking is recommended.

Q ⇌ ❀◁ 🚌 ♣ P ⊬

Radnorshire Arms
85 Bargates, HR6 8HB
☎ (01568) 613872
5-11; 12-11 Sat; 12-11 Sun
Adnams Bitter; guest beer

Workaday locals' two-bar pub, a short walk from the town centre. It has a small lounge and a well-appointed public bar with TV, and a separate elevated area with gaming machines. Laurel & Hardy keep watch over the lounge. Run with a real love by the landlady, the guest beers are sourced from local micro-breweries including Spinning Dog. A short walk from the town's best fish & chip shop.

🏚 Q ▣ 🚌 ♣

Royal Oak
South Street, HR6 8JA
☎ (01568) 612610
11-3, 6-11; 11-11 Sat; 12-3, 6-10.30 Sun
Shepherd Neame Spitfire; Wye Valley Butty Bach; guest beer

An old coaching inn, sympathetically restored and divided into two drinking areas, one with a real fire, and a separate restaurant. It has a deserved reputation for good food, both as bar snacks, particularly sandwiches, and full meals. The accommodation includes a Georgian four-poster bed.

🏚 Q ⇋ ◁🌒 ⇌ 🚌 P ⊬

Talbot Hotel
West Street, HR6 8EP
☎ (01568) 616347
11-2.30, 6-11; 12-2, 7-10.30 Sun
Greene King Ruddles Best Bitter

Large central hotel with two-bars; the lounge is comfortable with a real fire and the public is quiet and cosy. The hotel has absorbed a number of buildings in West Street and South Street including a saddlery and a former pub which may have served for a while as a back bar to the hotel. Food ranges from bar snacks to full table d'hôte and à la carte menus in the two restaurants.

🏚 Q ⇋◁🌒 ▣ ♿ ⇌ 🚌 P ⊬

Three Horseshoes
Corn Square, HR6 8LR
☎ (01568) 613019
10.30-11 daily
Brains Best Bitter

A fine example of a timber-framed pub overhanging the lane below, this early seventeenth century single-bar pub has etched windows of Victorian origin. On the market square it gets busy on Fridays (market day) and can get noisy in the evenings. Food is available all day. Free parking nearby.

🏚 ◁🌒 ⇌ 🚌 ♣ ⊬

White Lion

Etnam Street, HR6 8AE

☎ (01568) 612422

12-11.30; 12-11 Sun

Greene King Abbot

A recently refurbished and much improved two-bar black and white pub. The smaller bar is quiet and is used as a restaurant, whilst the larger has TV and a pool table in an adjoining room. Traditional pub food is served. The large garden hosts occasional events for families. The nearest of the town's pubs to the railway station.

❀ ◖❱ ⇌ 🚌 ♣ P

Goldmine

HR3 6DH On A438

☎ (01544) 327304

Previously the Swan Inn. Temporarily closed following a makeover and unsuccessful name change. Has normally offered real ale and food.

Duke of York

HR6 0JW On A4112, in village

☎ (01568) 750230

11.30-2.30; 7-midnight

No real ale or cider

This three roomed, stone built pub, once a farm-house, has been added to the CAMRA National Inventory of Historic Pub Interiors. The public bar has a stone fireplace, a fine curved settle, and the name of the pub spelt out in horse brasses. A small games room is to one side. The lounge is smartly furnished, in a timeless mix of settees, chairs and tables, plus a piano, grandfather clock and woodburner. A folk jam session is held on the first Wednesday of the month.

🏠 Q ❀ ◖ ♿ ♣ P

Royal George

SY7 0DY N of B4362 and S of A4113

OS 366669

☎ (01544) 267322

6-11; 12-11 Sat; 12-10.30 Sun

Wye Valley Bitter, Butty Bach; guest beer

A remote pub set in beautiful surroundings with a large and very pleasant garden. It has one

large bar, split into a public and an eating area resplendent with a wood burning stove. Home-prepared bar snacks, including tapas, available weekend lunchtimes and evening meals Thu-Sat. The original home of the Dunn Plowman Brewery back in the mid 1980's.

🏠 Q ❀ ❱ ♣ P

Alma Inn

HR9 7RY   Off B4221, W of M50 Jct3

OS 659255

☎ (01989) 720355

www.almainnlinton.co.uk

12-3 (not Mon-Fri), 6.30 (6 Fri & Sat)-11; 12-3, 7-10.30 Sun

Butcombe Bitter; RCH Pitchfork; guest beers (2)

Herefordshire CAMRA Pub of the Year most years since 2001, and joint winner again in 2005! The Alma is an enigma - a very successful village pub that thrives without serving food. A large, but cosy, lounge with roaring fire contrasts with a basic pool room, and a less-used non-smoking 'other room'. Run with real passion, the Alma champions smaller and local breweries. There's always something going on, and people from far and wide enjoy it as their local. The extensive hillside gardens to the rear host for an ambitious Blues & Ale festival held each June or July.

🏠 Q ❀ ⚠ ♣ P ⊀

Castle

HR2 8BB In village OS 508321

☎ (01981) 540756

Closed for some while, but due to reopen following refurbishment. Is expected to offer real ales and food.

Three Horseshoes Inn

HR7 4RQ OS 604509

☎ (01885) 400276

www.threehorseshoes.co.uk

11-3, 6.30-midnight (1 Fri, Sat); 12-4, 7-midnight Sun (closed Sun eve in Winter)

Greene King Old Speckled Hen; Marston Pedigree; Wye Valley Bitter: Olivers Perry

This pleasant country inn was, until 1900, a blacksmiths shop. Now open-plan, the single large bar serves a lounge, public/games area, a garden room and a restaurant, as well as the gardens outside. Customers are a good mix of diners and locals, including those involved in five various pub teams. A varied and interesting range of bar and restaurant meals is offered - booking recommended at weekends. Pensioners Pie & Pudding on Thursday: Bottled Olivers Cider is sold.

🍴 Q ⊛⇆ ◑ ⅋ Λ ♣ ● P ⅍

LITTLE DEWCHURCH — D6

Plough
HR2 6PW OS 535318
☎ (01432) 840273
11-midnight (1 Fri,Sat); 12-10.30 Sun
Flowers IPA; Wye Valley Butty Bach

A wayside inn on the `back` road from Ross to Hereford, dating from the early 19th century. The single bar, furnished in simple public-bar style, has a pool room to one side. Linked to the pub is the Ursa Major Restaurant, from which meals may be served in the pub itself. Home prepared and locally sourced, these include snacks and main meals, with a large vegetarian selection.

🍴 Q ⊛◑ ⅋ ⅍ 🚐 ♣ P

LITTLE HEREFORD — E2

Temeside Hotel
SY8 4AT On A456, W of village
☎ (01584) 711070
12-3, 6-11 daily (11-11 Sat; 12-11 Sun in summer)
Hobsons Best Bitter; Wye Valley HPA (summer): Westons Cider (summer)

The parish of Little Hereford lies in the far north of the county – and, where the main road enters the county briefly and crosses the River Teme, is the Temeside Inn. Only a pub since 1970, although of much earlier date, it has a spacious public bar with family area and pool table, and a lounge bar set out mainly as a restaurant. Outside, the garden goes right down to the banks of the river. Traditional home-made pub fare is offered with an accent on steaks and grills.

🍴 Q ⛵⊛◑ ⅋ ♣ ● P ⅍

LLANGROVE — D8

Royal Arms
HR9 6EZ In village OS 524194
☎ (01989) 770267
12-2, 6-11 (not Mon); 12-3, 6-11 Sat; 12-3, 6-10.30 Sun
Draught Bass; guest beer (occasional)

A lively village pub supporting darts and pool teams, it was originally a smithy, first called the Smiths Arms, but renamed in honour of Queen Victoria. A single bar serves a small public bar area with pool table and a larger lounge/restaurant. Tasty home-made food is served (not Sun eves). Children are welcome. The guest beer is often from a local brewery. Opens Bank Holiday Mondays, but closes all day on following Tuesdays.

🍴 Q ⊛◑ ⅋ P

LONGTOWN — B7

Crown
HR2 0LT In village OS 326285
☎ (01873) 860217

Temporarily closed, but scheduled to reopen before this guide is published. It is expected to offer real ale and food.

LOWER BULLINGHAM — D5

Wye Inn
Holme Lacy Road, HR2 6EF On B4399
☎ (01432) 270627
12-3, 5-11; 12-midnight Fri,Sat; 12-11 Sun
Brains SA; John Smiths Cask

A late Victorian roadhouse, fitted out in Whitbread open-plan 'Rustic' style. The large bar leads to a restaurant area and a children's play area. Facilities include an indoor children's play area, a full disabled toilet and a baby changing room. A varied range of pub food is available, with a carvery on Sunday (booking advised). No food Sun and Mon evenings; senior citizens specials on Thursday.

🏠 ⊛ ◑ ▶ ᚼ ♣ P

LUGWARDINE   E5

Crown & Anchor

Cotts Lane, HR1 4AB Just north of A438, in village

☎ (01432) 851303

12-11.30; 12-midnight Fri, Sat; 12-11.30 Sun

Butcombe Bitter; Taylor Landlord; Worthington Bitter; guest beers (2)

Dating from the early 18th century, this timber-framed black and white building houses two-bars with a variety of eating and drinking areas, including an attractive front garden. The large fireplace makes it very welcoming in winter. Food is home-prepared, ranging from traditional pub fare to a very interesting à la carte menu.

🏠 Q ⊛ ◑ ▶ 🚍 P ⅍

LUSTON   D2

Balance

HR6 0EB On B4361, in village

☎ (01568) 611134

12-3 (not winter), 7-11; 12-3, 6.30-11 Sat; 12-3, 7-10.30 Sun

Fullers London Pride; Greene King Abbot; Hobsons Best Bitter; Wye Valley Butty Bach

Located on the site of an old wool weighing station (therefore its name) in a small village, this pub has recently been refurbished to a high standard. The public bar has a pool table, dart board and television, whilst the main bar serves two small rooms and a conservatory furnished with settees. Traditional English meals with locally-sourced ingredients are served in the bar and adjoining restaurant.

🏠 ⊛ ◑ ▶ 🕮 ᚼ 🚍 ♣ P

LYONSHALL   B3

Royal George

HR5 3JN On A480, in village

☎ (01544) 340074

www.theroyalgeorgeinn.co.uk

12-2.30 (not Mon), 7-11; 11-midnight Fri; 12-midnight Sat; 12-2.30, 7-10.30 Sun

Black Sheep Bitter; guest beer

The timber-frame of this 16th century inn is hidden externally by rendering, but the beams

are much in evidence inside. There are two separate bars and a restaurant, adorned with photographs of local village life. Traditional home prepared, locally sourced food is served (not Sun, Mon evenings). The guest beer comes from local breweries.

🏠 ⊛ ◑ ▶ 🕮 ᚼ 🚍 ♣ P ⅍

MADLEY   C5

Comet

HR2 9NJ On B4352, SE of village

☎ (01981) 250600

www.thecometinn.co.uk

12-3, 6-11; 12-11 Sat, Sun

Hook Norton Hooky Best; guest beer

This roadside pub, some distance from the village at Woodyatt's Cross, is open plan, but divided into distinct sections served from a central bar. There are areas for pool and darts, a family area plus a restaurant in the conservatory. Traditional bar and full meals are served. The guest beer is usually from Wye Valley.

🏠 🏠 ⊛ ◑ ▶ ᚼ ⊿ 🚍 ♣ P ⅍

Red Lion

HR2 9PH In village, on B4352

☎ (01981) 250292

11-2.30, 5.30-11; 12-2.30, 5.30-10.30 Sun

Banks's Bitter; Marstons Pedigree

Two-bar black and white village pub, popular with locals. The unspoilt public bar is furnished in basic style and has an interesting alcove and separate games room. The lounge is more comfortably furnished, and, together with the separate restaurant, is used to serve the home-prepared meals (not Sun eve).

🏠 Q 🏠 ⊛ 🖾 ◑ ▶ 🕮 🚍 ♣ P

MARDEN   D4

Volunteer

HR1 3ET North edge of village OS 522478

☎ (01432) 880342

11-midnight; 12-midnight Sun

Worthington Bitter; guest beer

A pleasant two-bar village pub, popular with the locals, and supporting local football and cricket teams. The main bar is the public, with two drinking areas, pool table and dart board, whilst the no-smoking lounge also serves as a family room. Traditional bar snacks are available. The guest beer is from regional or national breweries.

♨ ⛵ ❀ ◑ ▌ ⬚ ♿ ⚠ 🚐 ♣ P ⚡

MATHON   G4

Cliffe Arms

WR13 5PW In village OS 737458

This attractive multi-roomed pub, parts of which date back to about 1400, has been closed for several years. No attempt has been made to change it to residential use.

MICHAELCHURCH ESCLEY   B6

Bridge Inn

HR2 0JW OS 318341

☎ (01981) 510646

12-3 (summer), 6-late; 11-late Sat; 12-11 Sun

Wye Valley Butty Bach; guest beer: Single changing draught cider

Dating from the 16th century, and beautifully situated by Escley brook, the Bridge has beamed ceiling, and an inglenook fireplace separating the family room from the main bar. Home-prepared food, much locally-sourced, is served in the bars and in the separate restaurant. The guest beer is mainly from Wye Valley and the cider from Gwatkins. Caravan facilities on-site.

♨ ❀ ◑ ▌ ⬚ ♿ ⚠ ♣ ● P ⚡

MONKLAND   C3

Monkland Arms

HR6 9DE On A44, W end of village

☎ (01568) 720259

www.itsa5guys.com

12-3.30, 7-11; 12-3.30, 7-10.30 Sun

House beer; guest beer

Dating back 200 years, the then timber-framed Travellers Arms was renamed the Red Lion before burning down in 1910. Rebuilt in brick and tile, around the surviving chimney stacks, the pub renamed again. With a lounge/diner, public bar and sports bar, it serves a passing and local trade, extending a welcome to bikers. Breakfasts and traditional roasts and grills are served - not Sun eve, when a quiz is held. The house beer is from Carlsberg (Tetley).

♨ ⛵ ❀ ◑ ▌ ⬚ ♿ ♣ P ⚡

MORDIFORD   E5

Moon Inn

HR1 4LW On B4224, in village

☎ (01432) 870236

11.30-2.30 (3 Thu,Fri), 6.30-11; 11.30-11 Sat; 12-4,7-10.30 Sun

Wells Bombardier; Wye Valley Butty Bach

This excellent timbered village pub originated as a farmhouse some 400 years ago - becoming a coaching inn about 300 years ago. The extension, to provide a restaurant area adjoining the lounge, was recently constructed using old timbers. The pub is very close to a well-known local walk - the Mordiford Loop. Walkers and families are very welcome. The food is varied, and includes vegetarian and gluten-free options (not served Sun eve). Quiz night Tuesday.

♨ ❀ ◑ ▌ ⬚ ♿ ⚠ 🚐 ♣ P ⚡

MORETON-ON-LUGG   D4

Village Inn

HR4 8DE In village, off A49

(01432) 760069

12-2.30, 5-11 daily

Black Sheep Bitter; Hook Norton Hooky Bitter; house beer

An unusual phenomenon - a new pub in a village where there is no record of a previous pub. The Village Inn was recently converted from the old school room. The main bar is the lounge, splendidly furnished with leather sofas, and there is a small public bar with a dartboard, a dining room, and a restaurant upstairs. Traditional English food is served, lunchtime and evenings.

Q ♿ 🚐 ♣ P

MORTIMERS CROSS   C2

Mortimers Cross

HR6 9PD At A4110/B4362 junction

☎ (01568) 709212

11-11; 12-10.30 Sun

Greene King IPA; Shepherd Neame Spitfire

The original 1701 inn was destroyed by fire - the present building is much newer. More recently it has been refurbished to a high standard, with considerable use of oak panelling and flooring in the main bars. There is also a games room, a family restaurant with a well, and a function room. Outside is a large garden. Home-prepared bar snacks and à la carte meals are offered, with a carvery Wed/Sun lunchtimes and Sat eve. Disabled facilities.

♨ ⛵ ❀ ◑ ▌ ◑ ♿ ⚠ ♣ P ⚡

MUCH BIRCH — D6

Axe & Cleaver

HR2 8HU On A49, S of village
☎ (01981) 540203
11.30-3, 6-11; 12-3, 7-10.30 Sun
Marstons Pedigree

A substantially modernised 17th Century half-timbered roadside inn with a large lounge and restaurant. Locally-sourced, home-prepared bar snacks and à la carte meals are served. The regular Hereford-Ross bus (no.38) stops nearby. Camping and caravan facilities available.

♨ Q ⚙ ◑ 🅐 ⛺ 🎪 P ⚲

Pilgrim Hotel

Ross Road, HR2 8HJ On A49
(01981) 540742
www.pilgrimhotel.co.uk
11-11 daily
Wye Valley HPA

Built in 1867, as the vicarage for Much Birch, this substantial hotel has a smartly furnished bar with bare stone walls and part flagstone floor. Out through a small annexe to the restaurant, is a wide expanse of lawn with lovely views. Bar snacks are served at lunchtime, and à la carte menu both lunchtimes and evenings. The food is locally provided and home-made and dietary needs are catered for. Rare-breed steaks are a speciality. Seniors' lunch on Fridays. Drinkers welcome.

🛏 ⚙ 🛌 ◑ 🎪 P ⚲

MUCH COWARNE — F4

Fir Tree

HR7 4JN On A4103
☎ (01531) 640619
12-3, 6(5 Fri)-11; 12-11 Sat; 12-4, 7-11 Sun
Taylor Golden Best; guest beer

Ownership has returned to the Price family after a brief gap, and real ale, including local guest beers, has reappeared. Much enlarged since its early 19th century beer house origins, it consists of a public bar, lounge, restaurant and large function room with disco and skittle alley, which doubles as a family room. Steaks are a speciality on the menu (food not served Sun-Tue eves).

♨ 🛏 ⚙ ◑ 🅐 👤 🅐 ♣ P

MUCH DEWCHURCH — D6

Black Swan

HR2 8DJ On B4348, in village
☎ (01981) 540295
12-3, 5.30-11; 12-4, 6-10.30 Sun,

Hook Norton Hooky Bitter; Taylor Landlord; guest beers (2): Westons 1st Quality cider

A most interesting and delightful 15th century heavily-beamed pub, complete with a priest hole. A small lounge leads into a dining room with open fire, and to a public bar with flag-stoned floor leading on through to a games room. Food is available every session, and Sunday lunches are remarkably substantial. Thursday night is folk night. The guest beers are mainly from regional breweries. Local bottled cider/perry is always available.

♨ ⚙ ◑ 🅐 🅐 ♣ 🍴 P

MUCH MARCLE — F6

Royal Oak

HR8 2ND On A449, NE of village
☎ (01531) 660300
www.royal-oak-inn.com
12-3, 6-11; 12-3, 7-10.30 Sun
Courage Directors, John Smiths Bitter

This roadside pub has its origins in a 19th century beer house, but is much extended. There is an all-dining lounge and, in the original part of the building, a public bar with pool table and bookcase full of old books. The latter converts to extra dining as required, and there is also a skittle alley/function room and fully equipped disabled toilet. Traditional pub fare is served.

⚙ 🛌 ◑ 🅐 🅐 ♣ 🍴 P ⚲

Slip Tavern

Watery Lane, HR8 2NG W of A449, towards Rushall OS 651333
☎ (01531) 660246

11.30-3 (not Mon), 6.-11; 12-3, 7-10.30 Sun

Woods Quaff; guest beers (2): Westons Old Rosie or Organic Cider (summer)

The pub name derives from a landslide in 1575 which buried the church and a herd of cattle (see plaque in entrance hall). The pub consists of a main bar area with real fire, plus a dining area, all set in very attractive gardens. Folk music evenings are held on the first Thursday of the month. The food (not served Sun/Mon evenings) is mostly English, with some international cuisine. Well-behaved children are welcome in the dining area. A guest beer is often from Whittingtons, and bottled Lyne Down cider and Perry is sold.

🏠 ❀ ◖◗ 🍎 🍺 P ✶

Walwyn Arms

HR8 2LY On A449, at B4024 junction
☎ (01531) 660758

12-2.30, 5-11; 12-11 Fri, Sat; 12-10.30 Sun

Greene King IPA; Shepherd Neame Spitfire; guest beer: Westons Old Rosie cider

A 17th century village pub, which for many years doubled as a butcher's shop and slaughterhouse. It now consists of a single large bar and a small alcove to the side, with settle, a small dining room and skittle alley/function room. Home cooked, locally-sourced traditional bar snacks and meals are served (not after 6pm Sunday). Families are welcome, but away from the bar.

🏠 ❀ ◖◗ 🍀 🍺 P ✶

MUNSTONE   D5

Rose Gardens

Coldwells Road, HR1 1LH N of A4103, W end of village OS 513426

☎ (01432) 267803

No real ale or cider

A pleasant country pub just to the north of the city, with a large garden and open-air play area for children.

NEWTOWN   F5

Newtown Inn

HR8 2UG On A4103, near A417 junction
☎ (01531) 670423

11.30-3, 5.30-11 (not Mon in winter); 12-3.30, 7-10.30 Sun

Greene King IPA, Abbot; guest beer

A very old inn, much extended and recently refurbished to a high standard, consisting of a bar and split level dining area. Although very close to the main Worcester to Hereford road, the main entrance is safely tucked away to the rear - off the car park. All food is freshly prepared, traditional fayre including lunchtime specials. Interesting 'sign post' pub sign.

🏠 Q ❀ 🛏 ◖◗ ♿ 🍀 P

NORTON CANON   C4

Three Horseshoes

HR4 7BH On A480
☎ (01544) 318375

12-3 (Wed, Sat only), 6-11; 12-3, 7-10.30 Sun

Shoes Norton Ale, Canon Bitter, Peploe's Tipple, Farriers Beer

Recovering from a major fire in March 2006, that left the bars largely unscathed, it is home to Shoes Brewery. A public bar leads through to a larger pool room, in contrast to a small cosy lounge, furnished with an ad hoc collection of comfortable old sofas, chairs and a piano. Farriers Beer at 15.4% ABV, is now available on draught as well as in bottles. The bus stop is half mile from the pub (services 461/462 from Hereford), alight at the 'Weobley Turn'.

🏠 Q ☕ ❀ 🍺 🚌 🍀 P

ORCOP   D7

Fountain

Orcop Hill, HR2 8EP OS 480469
☎ (01981) 540304

This small traditional village pub is currently closed. In recent times it has offered both real ale and food.

ORLETON   D2

Boot

SY8 4HN   Off B4361, in village   OS 494672
☎ (01568) 780228
12-3, 6-11; 12-3, 7-11 Sun

Hobsons Best Bitter, Town Crier; guest beer

Popular 17th century black and white village pub with distinctive and comfortable public bar, lounge and restaurant. A large, attractive beer garden includes a children's play area and a barbecue. The home-cooked food ranges from bar snacks to à la carte with interesting daily specials. A charity quiz is held monthly on a Tuesday in winter. The guest beer is from mainly local breweries; local bottled cider is stocked.

🏠 Q ✿ ◑ ▮ 🚌 ♣ P

Maidenhead

SY8 4JB   On B4361
☎ (01584) 831686
12-3, 6-11; 12-3, 7-10.30 Sun

Greene King Ruddles Best Bitter; guest beer

An attractive and friendly two-bar roadside inn dating from the 17th century with later, stone built additions to the rear. The public bar has a flagstone floor and a games area with pool table, well away from drinkers. The lounge has a dining area. Home-cooked bar snacks and main meals are served (not Sun eves).

🏠 Q ✿ ◑ ▮ ⬚ ♿ ⚠ 🚌 ♣ P

PEMBRIDGE   C3

King's House

East Street, HR6 9HB
☎ (01544) 388029
www.kingshouseinn.co.uk
12-3, 6-11; 12-3, 6-10.30 Sun

Beer range varies (2)

Named after a wealthy local merchant, Robert King, this is a 15th century building of interesting construction with close-set timber framing. Previously the Greyhound, it was delicensed for some years. Now primarily a restaurant, it offers a variety of local real ales.

🏠 ✿ 🛏 ◑ ▮ ♿ 🚌

New Inn

Market Square, HR6 9DZ
☎ (01544) 388427
11-3, 6-11; 12-3, 7-10.30 Sun,

Black Sheep Bitter; Dunn Plowman Brewhouse Bitter; Fullers London Pride: Westons Old Rosie cider

This imposing and very genuine old building faces on to the market square, where outdoor seating is available. Facilities include a public bar, resplendent with flagstone floor, large settle and large fireplace; lounge bar, a separate eating/drinking/family area, and a downstairs restaurant. The heavily-beamed interior is decorated with hopbines and a variety of traditional furniture gives a homely atmosphere. Games include shove ha'penny. A wide selection of malt whiskies is also available, plus bottled Dunkerton's Black Fox cider.

🏠 Q ❧ ✿ 🛏 ◑ ▮ ⬚ 🚌 ♣ P

Red Lion

High Street, HR6 9DS
☎ (01544) 387901
redlion@mediaeval-pembridge.com
12-3, 6-11; 12-11 Sat; 12-10.30 Sun

Greene King IPA; Wye Valley Butty Bach; guest beer

Sympathetically refurbished and retaining original timbers, this pub has a large single bar screened off into what may be loosely described as drinking and dining areas. A small beer garden at high level to the side, backs on to the churchyard, with its distinctive tower. One guest beer is usually from a local brewery. Light lunches and bar snacks are served using locally-sourced produce. A quiz is held on Tuesdays, and bingo on Thursdays.

🏠 ✿ ◑ ▮ ⬚ 🚌 ♣ P ✄

PENCOMBE   E4

Wheelwrights

HR7 4RN   In village   OS 598528
☎ (01885) 400358
12-2.30 (not Mon), 6-11; 12-4, 7-10.30 Sun

Adnams Broadside; Cotleigh Tawny; Greene Old Speckled Hen; Taylor Landlord; guest beer

Excellent and sympathetically-modernised 17th century single-bar establishment that is everything a thriving village pub should be. At the centre of its community, it won Herefordshire CAMRA Country Pub of the Year 2003. There is always something going on to complement the ales. Straightforward value pub food (Wed-Suns) contrasts with the rare breeds steak nights (booking advised). Folk and poetry jam session on the first Tuesday of the month.

P

PETERCHURCH B5

Boughton Arms

HR2 0RT On B4348, in village
(01981) 550208
12-2, 5-11; 12-11 Fri-Sun
Wild Night; guest beer

Village pub consisting of a large U-shaped public bar, flanked by two separate games areas, and a small lounge and restaurant. The guest beers (two in summer) are from local breweries. Home-cooked traditional snacks and meals, are provided all day with interesting specials and a soup menu. Families are welcome.

P

Nags Head

HR2 0SJ On B4348, at NW end of village
(01981) 550179
10-11; 12-10.30 Sun
Hook Norton Hooky Bitter

Friendly, strictly no-frills village local, with a single bar, a quiet snug and separate dining area. The good value bar snacks use all local meat and Portuguese speciality meals are available, if pre-ordered. Pub games, including petanque, are important at the pub, and a number of teams operate.

P

PETERSTOW E7

Red Lion

Winters Cross, HR9 6LH On A49, W of village
(01989) 730202
12-2.30, 6-11.30(12.30 Fri, Sat); 12-12.30am Sat; 12-11 Sun
Otter Bitter; Taylor Landlord; guest beers (2)

The Red Lion was delicensed in the 1970s but, unusually, reverted to a pub a few years later - after a sympathetic renovation. A single bar serves drinking and dining areas, including a conservatory. The home-prepared food ranges from bar snacks to full meals, many of which are offered as a 'light bite' option: booking is advised at most times. Guest beers from local micros or regional breweries. Facilities include an outdoor adventure playground for children. The regular Hereford-Ross bus service (no. 38) stops outside.

P

Yew Tree

HR9 6JZ On A49, in village
(01989) 562815
12-3, 6-11 (midnight Thu-Sat); 12-3, 6-10.30 Sun
Flowers IPA; guest beer (not winter)

A single bar serves a public with original stone fireplace and pool table, and a separate dining area. This friendly pub mainly serves the passing trade at lunchtimes, and is very much a locals' pub in the evening. Traditional home-cooked pub food is served (not Thu/Sun eves). Live music some weekends. Camping/caravan site available. Hereford-Ross bus service 38 stops in village. Opens all day in summer.

P

PRESTON ON WYE C5

Yew Tree

HR2 9JT In village OS 385414
(01981) 500359
7-midnight (1am Fri, Sat); 12-3, 7-11 Sun
Single changing beer [G]

A pleasantly eccentric and unspoilt single-bar drinkers' establishment located in a quiet hamlet near the River Wye. Comfortable and welcoming, it supports boules, pool and quiz teams, whilst in the summer, it is popular with fishermen and canoeists. The beer, which tends to alternate from local or regional breweries, is served direct from a cask behind the small bar. Draught Thatchers Heritage Cider is also available. Probably open additionally on Saturday lunchtimes in summer; it also hosts monthly live music on Saturdays.

Q P

PRIORS FROME — E5

Yew Tree

HR1 4EH In village, or direct off Dormington - Mordiford road OS 575390
☎ (01432) 850467
www.lengees.info
12-2, 7-11 (closed Tues); 12-2, 6-11 Thu, Fri; 12-4, 6-11 Sat, Sun

Greene King Ruddles Best; Spinning Dog Hereford Organic; guest beer: Prospect Farm Cider [G]

Home of the popular and well-regarded Len Gee's restaurant - this pub also caters well for locals. Due to its hillside setting, the public and lounge bars are at front door level, while the restaurant is lower - at car park level at the back. If using the restaurant, note that the real ales are upstairs. The patio has excellent views over the valley where the Rivers Frome, Lugg and Wye meet. On quieter days the home-cooked, locally-sourced meals are served in the lounge, whilst at weekends it is advisable to book for the extensive menu or carvery. Guest beer usually from micro-breweries.

🏨 ❀ ◖ ▮ ⊞ ♿ ♣ 🐾 P ✂

RHYDSPENCE — A4

Rhydspence Inn

Whitney on Wye, HR3 6EU On A438
☎ (01497) 831262
11-2.30, 7-11; 12-2.30, 7-10.30 Sun

Draught Bass; Robinson's Best Bitter: Dunkerton's Cider (summer)

A large timber framed pub, set imposingly right on the Welsh border. This beautifully positioned 14th century drovers' inn retains many original features. The emphasis now is on high quality food and accommodation, but drinkers are still welcome. An architectural gem, consisting of a public bar, lounge bar and restaurant, it is totally free from piped music and other distractions. Bottled Dunkerton's Cider is available at all times.

🏨 Q ➤ ❀ 🛏 ◖ ▮ ⊞ 🐾 P ✂

RICHARD'S CASTLE — D2

Castle

Castle Road, SY8 4EW On B4361, in village
☎ (01584) 831678
6-11; 11-11 Sat; 12-3; 7-10.30 Sun
Banks's Bitter; Hobsons Best; guest beer

A pleasant village local with a basic, brightly-lit, but welcoming public bar - complete with real fire. The panelled lounge bar doubles as a dining room for the home-cooked Sunday lunches, which use locally-reared meats (no food at any other times). The separate pool room is closed Sunday lunchtime. There is also a well-kept garden with picnic tables.

🏨 Q ❀ ◖ ▮ ♿ ⊞ ♣ P

ROSS-ON-WYE — E7

Barrel

Brookend Street, HR9 7EG
☎ (01989) 769660
No real ale or cider

A typical young people's games pub.

Chase Hotel

Gloucester Road, HR9 5LH
☎ (01989) 763161
www.chasehotel.co.uk
11-11 daily
Draught Bass

Large Georgian building - now a hotel with a quiet bar, comfortable lounge, large garden and conference/function rooms. An impressive menu of bar snacks and meals is available, as well as a full à la carte menu in Harry's Restaurant. All dietary requirements catered for.

Q ➤ ❀ 🛏 ◖ ▮ ♿ ⊞ P ✂

Connollys

7 Gloucester Road, HR9 5BU
☎ (01989) 769994
No real ale or cider

Irish theme pub, previously the Kings Arms.

Crown & Sceptre

Market Place, HR9 5HX
☎ (01989) 562765
10-midnight (1am Fri, Sat); 12-10.30 Sun

Wye Valley Bitter; guest beer (2): Westons Old Rosie cider

Seventeenth century drinking house positioned proudly on the old market place. Scrubbed tables and sofas at front of house, give way to a long narrow bar with a clean refectory feel, plus a pool and games area at the rear. This pub is popular with all, but the younger set dominates weekend evenings when it can get very loud and busy. Modern-

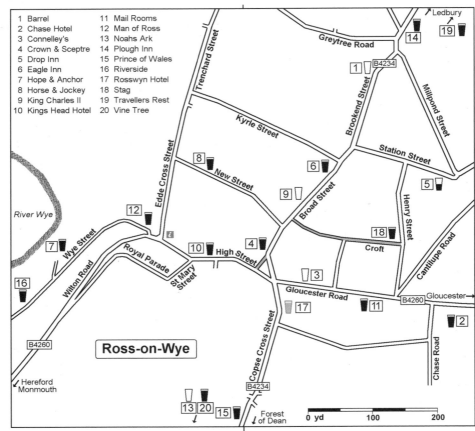

1	Barrel	11	Mail Rooms
2	Chase Hotel	12	Man of Ross
3	Connelley's	13	Noahs Ark
4	Crown & Sceptre	14	Plough Inn
5	Drop Inn	15	Prince of Wales
6	Eagle Inn	16	Riverside
7	Hope & Anchor	17	Rosswyn Hotel
8	Horse & Jockey	18	Stag
9	King Charles II	19	Travellers Rest
10	Kings Head Hotel	20	Vine Tree

Ross-on-Wye

style bar food is available all day, including a children's menu. Guest beers from regional breweries.

Drop Inn

21 Station Street, HR9 7AG

☎ (01989) 563256

11-2, 5-midnight; 11-midnight Fri, Sat; 12-midnight Sun

Single changing beer.

Arrangements were in hand, as this guide was printed, to reintroduce real ale for the first time for many years, in what was previously the Queens Head. Behind the interesting pub sign, is a single-bar pub with pool table and skittle alley.

Eagle Inn

23 Broad Street, HR9 7EA

☎ (01989) 562652

www.simplyleisureuk.com

8am-11.30; 8am-1.30am Fri/Sat; 8am-11.30 Sun

Greene King IPA; Shepherd Neame Spitfire; Wychwood Hobgoblin

An eighteenth century inn known as the New Inn until 1969, when, after extensive modernisation, it was renamed topically after the Apollo 11 Lunar Module. It now consists of a wood panelled L-shaped bar with pool table, a restaurant and function room, and a further restaurant, accessed by a spiral staircase. Food is available all day - ranging from snacks to full meals in modern British style. This pub is quiet by day, but has loud juke box music in the evening.

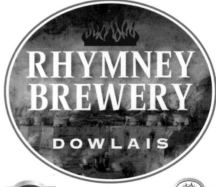

Hope & Anchor
Rope Walk, HR9 7BU
☎ (01989) 563003
12-11; 12-midnight Fri, Sat; 12-11 Sun
Banks's Original; Marstons Old Empire; guest beer

A popular pub, superbly situated facing the River Wye, with a long history involving rope-making, basket making and pleasure boats. The front door leads to a drinking area with a flagstone floor and a boat hanging from the ceiling. On the left is the wood-panelled bar, also in the shape of a boat. On the other side, at a higher level, are the pub's dining areas. Mainly home made snacks and meals are served, and children are welcome. Live music Wed/Fri. Picnic tables line the river bank area in front of the pub.

Horse & Jockey
9-10 New Street, HR9 7DA
☎ (01989) 763834
11-11; 11-midnight Thu - Sat; 12-10.30 Sun
Draught Bass: Westons Old Rosie [G]

An early nineteenth century pub, just off the town centre, opposite the old gaol. The single bar serves an L-shaped drinking area, parti-tioned into lounge and public bar – with a pool table at the far end. Homemade bar snacks are served, with a roast on Sunday.

King Charles II
13 Broad Street, HR9 7EA
☎ (01989) 562039
No real ale or cider

A large old coaching inn on the main street, which has been opened out and much altered. Now a night club.

Kings Head Hotel
8 High Street, HR9 5HL
☎ (01989) 763174
www.kingshead.co.uk
11-11; 12-10.30 Sun
Wye Valley Bitter; guest beer

Large central hotel, once a coaching inn, that is claimed to date from the 14th century. However, the Kings Bar (the real ale bar) is of Georgian origin, with pine panelling. The restaurant to the

rear has a 60-foot deep well as its centrepiece. A varied menu of bar snacks and meals are served, as well as coffee and afternoon tea. Different Wye Valley beers may be served, and the guest is local.

Mail Rooms
Gloucester Road, HR9 5BS
☎ (01989) 760920
9-midnight (1am Fri, Sat)
Greene King Abbot; Marston Pedigree; guest beers (2): Westons Old Rosie, Organic Vintage cider [G]

Typical J D Wetherspoons conversion of a former post office into a modern, well-lit and comfortably-furnished large single bar, with two non-smoking areas. Excellent value food available all day. Full disabled facilities.

Man of Ross
Wye Street, HR9 7BS
☎ (01989) 564597
11-11 (midnight Thu-Sat); 12-11 Sun
Draught Bass; Greene King IPA

Comfortable two-room town local dating from Jacobean times, named after the town's great benefactor, John Kyrle (1637-1724). The main entrance to the public bar is in the single sto-rey section under a high curved gable. The lounge bar is served via a hatch from the main bar. Bar snacks and traditional Sunday lunches are served.

Noahs Ark
7 Chapel Road, Tudorville, HR9 5PR
☎ (01989) 563060
No real ale or cider

Suburban local, just off the main road.

Plough Inn
Over Ross Street, HR9 7AS
☎ (01989) 566484
5.30-11; 11-11.30 Sat; 12-10.30 Sun
Draught Bass; Brains Reverend James

This interesting local dates from the eighteenth century with bare stone walls and much origi-nal timber, most notably including the front door. There is one main bar, plus a separate quiet room and a skittle alley. Children are welcome. Bingo on Wednesday evenings.

🏚 Q 🕸 ♿ 🚌 ♣

Prince of Wales
Walford Road, HR9 5AP
☎ (01989) 562517
11.30-3, 6.30-11; 11.30-11 Sat; 12-10.30 Sun
Draught Bass; Marstons Pedigree; guest beer: Westons Old Rosie cider

Pleasant locals' pub dating from the 19th century. Much alteration resulted in a single, large, L-shaped bar roughly divided into a lounge, pool room and restaurant. There is a large function room to the rear. Snacks are served at lunchtime, with full dining in the evenings and traditional Sunday lunches.

🏚 🛏 🕸 ◖ ♿ 🚌 ♣ 🍺 P ✂

Riverside
20 Wye Street, HR9 7BT
☎ (01989) 564688
www.wyenot.com/riverside
11-11; 12-10.30 Sun
Freeminer Bitter; Iron Brew: Gwatkins and Black Rat cider

Delightfully situated by the Wye, the single bar has views of the river, and outdoor drinking may be enjoyed on a large expanse of the river bank. Recently refurbished with modern flagstone floors throughout, and enjoying a large decked area outside. Games are important, with a pool table and darts in the lively bar. Traditional snacks can be taken in the bar or the separate dining room. Large car parks are nearby, plus limited free on-street parking. Live music Fridays and Sundays.

🕸 🛏 ◖ ♿ 🚌 ♣ 🍺 ✂

Rosswyn Hotel
High Street, HR9 5BZ

Town centre hotel with interesting carved wall panelling; closed after fire damage and subject to change-of-use planning application.

Stag
5 Henry Street, HR9 7AA
☎ (01989) 562893
10-11; 12-10.30 Sun

Wells Bombardier; guest beer: Bulmers Traditional cider

Popular back-street two-bar local with a friendly atmosphere supporting many pub teams. Games include quoits and shove ha'penny. This pub once belonged to the Alton Court Brewery, which was just down the road. Limited on-street parking available. The guest beer may be from a regional or micro-brewery.

Q 🛋 🚌 ♣ 🍺

Travellers Rest
HR9 7QJ On A449/M50/B4221 junction
☎ (01989) 563861
11-11; 11-10.30
Banks's Bitter

The original pub on this site was demolished in 1960, when the M50 was built. The replacement, overlooking Junction 1, has a large open-plan bar fitted out in 'Rustic' Beefeater-style, with an adjoining Premier Travel Inn. Families are welcome, and there is a play area outside. Food is standard range for this chain, and aspirators are used on the beer. Full disabled facilities available. The car park is free for three hours for customers.

🛏 🕸 🛏 ◖ ♿ P ✂

Vine Tree
Walford Road, Tudorville, HR9 5RS On B4228
☎ (01989) 562882
12-2, 6-midnight; 12-midnight Sun
Sharps Doom Bar; Tetley's Bitter

Pleasant and popular locals' pub on the very edge of town, with public bar, lounge/restaurant and skittle alley. Traditional pub food is served, together with Sunday lunches. Adjoining Caravan Park

🛏 🕸 ◖ 🛋 ♿ ♣ 🍺 P

Ancient Camp
Eaton Bishop, HR2 9QX   OS 453393
☎ (01981) 250449

Idyllically situated pub and restaurant, with views across the River Wye. Previously reopened after a successful locals' campaign to see off a planning application that would have seen it converted to a private house in 2003, it is temporarily closed as this guide went to print.

ST OWENS CROSS   D7

New Inn
HR2 8LQ At A4137/B4521 Junction
☎ (01989) 730274
www.newinn.biz
11-midnight daily
Marstons Pedigree; guest beers: Broome Farm Cider

This black and white sixteenth century inn, an old favourite, has a timbered, split-level main bar, with cosy nooks and crannies and a large inglenook fireplace. The real ales, including guests from regional breweries, are served from a pewter beer engine rescued from a long defunct pub in Ross-on-Wye. Traditional English bar snacks and meals are served in the bar, dining room and in the child-friendly garden, with its fine views to the Black mountains. Accommodation includes a four-poster bed.

🏨 ❀ 🛏 ◖◗ 🅳 ⚠ 🖨 ♣ ☕ P

SELLACK   E7

Loughpool Inn
HR9 6LX 1 mile NW of A49 at Peterstow
OS 558268
☎ (01989) 730236
11.30-3, 6.30-11; 12-3, 7-10.30 Sun
Courage Best Bitter; Wye Valley Bitter, Butty Bach; guest beer

A superb example of a 16th-Century black and white half-timbered inn, set behind attractive lawns, with exceptional views over delightful countryside. The single long opened-out bar has the original flagstone floor, wooden tables and kitchen chairs. There is also a separate restaurant. The accent is unashamedly on food to a very high standard, using local produce where possible - but not to the exclusion of

drinkers. (Booking advisable for meals). The guest beer is usually local. Closed on Sunday and Monday evenings in the winter months.

🏨 Q ❀ ◖◗ 🅳 P

SHOBDON   C3

Bateman Arms
HR6 9LX In village, on B4362
☎ (01568) 708374
www.batemanarms.co.uk
12-2.30, 5-11;11-11 Sat; 11-10.30 Sun
Hook Norton Hooky Best; Wye Valley Butty Bach

An unusual three storey timber-framed, oak-panelled building that is mainly eighteenth century (some parts are older), that was given by the Bateman estate to the village. The main bar has a wood-burning stove and settle, and there is a restaurant and function/games room. An à la carte menu is available. Food is prepared using locally bought ingredients. The pub is near Herefordshire's only airfield - Shobdon Aerodrome. Hook Norton seasonal beers may substitute.

🏨 ❀ 🛏 ◖◗ ♣ P ⚟

STANFORD BISHOP   F4

Herefordshire House
Malvern Road, WR6 5TT On B4220
☎ (01886) 884252
No real ale or cider

A basic two-bar, isolated roadside pub, undergoing a protracted renovation, after which real ale may return.

STAPLOW   F5

Oak
HR8 1NP On B4214
☎ 7837 169970
7-11 Tues-Sat; 7-10.30 Sun
Goffs Jouster; guest beer

A roadside pub, once a cider house, with an open-plan public bar. The main bar is decorated with an eclectic mix of bric-a-brac, and has a separate games area offering pool, darts and table skittles. A more cosy lounge bar is situated in the single story part of the building, and is also used as a function room. The guest beer is normally from Mayfields. Reintroduction of food is planned.

🏨 Q ❀ 🍽 🅳 🖨 ♣ P

STAUNTON ON WYE   B4

New Inn

HR4 7LR In village, just N of A438 OS 365452
☎ (01981) 500346
12-3 (not Mon), 7-11; 12-3, 7-10.30 Sun
Wye Valley Bitter; guest beer (summer)

Popular sixteenth century village local at the heart of the community, with low ceilings in a single bar and a separate pool-cum-family room. Quoits and petanque are also played, with the teams' success evidenced by a display of trophies. The attractive beer garden has good views of the surrounding countryside. The guest beer is from local or regional breweries. Traditional bar snacks and meals are are served at lunchtime and Fri and Sat Eves. Roast on Sunday.

🛏 Q ☎ ❀ ◖◗ 🍴 🕭 ⌨ ♣ P

Portway Inn Hotel

Brecon Road, HR4 7NH On A438
☎ (01981) 500474
11-1am;11-1.30am Fri,Sat; 11-12.30am Sun
Brains SA; Courage Best; Wye Valley Butty Bach; guest beer

Dating from the sixteenth century, and once a drovers' inn, the Portway now offers plush, comfortable surroundings in its large lounge and restaurant. Snacks and main meals are available, the menu being a mix of traditional and modern - with daily specials and a Sunday carvery. The Wye Valley Walk passes nearby. Guest beer is usually from a local brewery.

🛏 Q ☎ ❀ ⊟ ◖◗ 🍴 🕭 ⌨ ♣ P ⊬

STIFFORDS BRIDGE   G4

Prancing Pony

WR13 5NN On A4103
☎ (01886) 880213
9-11; 11-10.30 Sun
Marstons Pedigree; guest beer

After two hundred years as the Seven Stars, its frontage now dominated by a large conservatory, the Prancing Pony has a bizarre mixture of architectural styles. The open-plan bar (with pool table) is furnished with an eccentric mix of pub furniture and sofas of varying ages. There is a separate restaurant to the side. Bar meals are available all day (except Sun eves) plus a Sunday carvery until 5pm. The only clue to its unusual name is a cowboy mannequin in the main bar.

🛏 ❀ ◖◗ ♣ P

Red Lion

WR13 5NN On A4103
☎ (01886) 880318
12-11; 12-10.30 Sun
Greene King IPA, Abbot; guest beer (summer)

Pleasantly situated by the Cradley Brook, this multi-roomed roadside pub has some character. It has a spacious bar and several dining areas, with modern flagstone floors, wood panelling and bare brick walls. Two large fireplaces house woodburners. The traditional, home-prepared English food is available all day, and is popular at weekends with diners from Malvern. The attractive garden is suitable for families. The guest beer is from the Greene King range.

🛏 ❀ ◖◗ 🕭 P ⊬

STOKE LACY   F4

Plough Inn

HR7 4HG In village, on A465
☎ (01885) 490658
11.30-2.30, 6.30-midnight Tue-Fri; 11.30-3, 6.30-midnight Sat; 12-3, 7-11 Sun,
Wye Valley Bitter, HPA, seasonal beer

A deceptively large pub, located adjacent to the Wye Valley Brewery. To the rear there is a small locals' bar, leading into a large function/games room. At the front, is a lounge bar and separate restaurant. Bar meals are always available with a traditional à la carte menu in the evening, plus Sunday lunches. Meals are freshly-prepared using local ingredients.

🛏 ☎ ❀ ◖◗ 🍴 🕭 ⌨ ♣ P

STOKE PRIOR — D3

Lamb Inn

HR6 0NB In village OS 521566
☎ (01568) 760308
12-3 (not Mon), 6.30-11(midnight Fri); 12-midnight
Sat; 12-10.30 Sun
Shepherd Neame Spitfire; guest beer
This village inn has a large, single bar with
games, and restaurant areas. Home prepared
traditional pub food and bar snacks are available except Sunday evenings, with vegetarian
options. Families are welcome. Guest beers are
from regional breweries.

🏚 ❀ ◖ ◗ 🚌 ✦ P ✗

STORRIDGE — G4

New Inn

WR13 5HB On A4103, 1 mile NE of village
☎ (01886) 832353
10-3, 6-11; 12-10.30 Sun
Banks's Bitter; Marstons Bitter, Pedigree (summer)
An isolated but friendly and traditional one-room
roadside pub straddling the border with Worcestershire, with basic decor, but a welcoming
atmosphere. The bar has traditional and electronic games and the locals take their dart playing seriously here. The garden has a children's
play area and there is camping in the field to the
rear. Traditional English food is served (not Sun
or Mon eves).

🏚 ❀ ◖ ◗ ⛺ 🚌 ✦ P

STRETTON SUGWAS — D5

Travellers Rest

HR4 7AL Just off A480/A4103 junction
☎ (01432) 760268
11-3, 6-11; 11-11 Fri,Sat; 12-3 7-10.30 Sun
Draught Bass
Popular creeper-clad, red brick pub, just hidden
from a new road junction. There is a lounge with
dining area serving freshly prepared food, and a
public bar, with separate area for the pool table,
where games are an important part of pub life.
Evening meals by advance booking only. It has
a pleasant garden, suitable for families.

🏚 ❀ ◖ ◗ 🍴 ♿ 🚌 ✦ P

SUTTON ST NICHOLAS — D4

Amberley Arms

HR1 3BX N of village. OS 541476

☎ (01432) 880789
6-11 (not Mon); 6-midnight Sat; 12-4, 7-10.30 Sun
Wye Valley Bitter, Butty Bach
Located north of the village of Sutton, this pub
has been renamed after the nearby parish of
Amberley. Dating from the 17th century, although much modernised, it has two bars, a
restaurant and a skittle alley. It is primarily a
locals' pub, and serves traditional pub food -
including takeaways.

🏚 ❀ ◖ ◗ 🍴 ♿ 🚌 ✦ P

Golden Cross

HR1 3AZ In village OS 533455
☎ (01432) 880274
www.goldencrossinn.com
12 - 3, 6 - midnight; Friday 12 - 3, 6 - 1am. Saturday
12noon - 1am, Sunday 12 - midnight
Hancocks HB; guest beer
Recently opened out and refurbished in contemporary style with a large main bar, complemented by a public bar area with pool, darts
and quoits. There is a restaurant upstairs serving a good selection of traditional and modern
cuisine, specialising in local steaks. These
meals plus snacks are also served in the bar.
Full disabled toilets and baby changing facilities.

🏚 Q ❀ ◖ ◗ 🍴 ♿ 🚌 ✦ P

SWAINSHILL — C5

Kite's Nest

HR4 7QA On A438
A 19th century red brick roadside pub, built on
the site of an older pub. Currently closed; it
has normally offered real ale and food.

SYMONDS YAT EAST — E8

Royal Hotel

HR9 6JL
☎ (01600) 890238
www.royalhotel-symondsyat.com
11-11; 12-10.30 Sun
Brains SA, Reverend James
Beautifully situated towards Yat Rock, the
Royal is very much a hotel, but has the 'Rap-
ids Bar', plus a lounge and restaurant open to
non-residents. Food is traditional British, locally sourced, with snacks served weekday
lunchtimes and all day at weekends plus restaurant meals in the evening. Walkers, cyclists
and canoeists are welcome but the car park is

pay-and-display for pub customers. The Reverend James is not available in winter.

㎖ ⮩ 🍴🛏 ◖ 🚻 Ⓟ 🚭

Saracens Head

HR9 6JL
☎ (01600) 890435
www.saracensheadinn.co.uk
11-11; 12-10.30 Sun
Greene King Old Speckled Hen; Theakston Best Bitter, Old Peculier; Wye Valley HPA, Butty Bach

A riverside inn that operates its own foot passenger ferry across the Wye when the pub is open. It has a large single bar with flagstone floor, pews, scrubbed wood tables and a working red telephone box. There is a lounge/dining room and a patio overlooking the river. A varied menu of freshly prepared bar snacks and full meals, including vegetarian, is on offer. An adjacent (public) car park is free in the evenings.

🍴🛏 ◖ 🚻 △ ♣

SYMONDS YAT WEST E8

Old Court Hotel

HR9 6DA On B4164
☎ (01600) 890367
www.oldcourthotel.co.uk
10-11; 10-midnight Fri, Sat; 10-11 Sun
Wye Valley Bitter; Brains Reverend James: Westons Old Rosie (summer)

A very fine stone-faced manor house of 1570, with two lounge bars and a restaurant in the superb Great Hall. The carved wooden bar is a notable feature. Home-cooked bar and à la carte menus are available, specialising in all locally grown produce. The guest beer is normally from the Wye Valley monthly range. There is a children's play area in the garden. Quiz night Tuesday in Winter.

㎖ ⮩ 🍴🛏 ◖ Ⓟ

Olde Ferrie Inne

Ferrie Lane, HR9 6BL Off B4164
☎ (01600) 890232
12-11; 12-midnight Fri, Sat; 12-11 Sun
Wye Valley HPA; Greene King IPA, Ruddles County

Claiming to date from the 15th century the Ferry Inn began as a beer house for bargees on the river Wye, and the pub still operates a ferry on an as-required basis (not in winter). The large lounge, restaurant and extensive patio offer superb river views. The locally sourced traditional style meals are characterised by generous portions. The car park may be pay and display on peak daytimes.

㎖ ⮩ 🍴🛏 ◖ ♣ Ⓟ

Wye Knot Inn

HR9 6BJ On B4164
☎ (01600) 890501
12-3, 6-11 (12-11 summer); 11-11 Sat; 12-11 Sun
Wye Valley HPA; Marstons Pedigree; guest beer

Originally the Grove Inn, it was also nicknamed the 'Jampots' (as it once served beer in jam pots, due to a wartime glass shortage). The original building has been much extended, and consists of a large lounge bar and restaurant, with a beer garden across the road. There are many interesting local photographs adorning the walls. The traditional bar snacks to full à la carte meals use local produce - Monday night features spiced dishes from around the world. Guest beers are local or regional.

㎖ 🍴🛏 ◖ Ⓟ 🚭

TARRINGTON E5

Tarrington Arms

HR1 4HX On A438, in village
☎ (01432) 890796
www.tarringtonarms.co.uk
12-3, 7-11; 12-3, 7-10.30 Sun
Wood Shropshire Lad; guest beer

Re-invented late Georgian red brick ex-hotel, with colonnade entrance, it has two bars and a restaurant with a distinctly refectory atmosphere. The smaller lounge bar has old photos of the hop-picking industry, and contrasts with an archetypal public bar. The guest beer is from small regional or micro breweries. The food strikes a rare a balance - of high standard but affordable, with a fish night each third Wednesday of the month. No food Sunday evenings. Hereford - Ledbury bus service 476 stops outside.

🏨 🐕 🛏 ◖◗ 🍴 🍺 ✚ P ✂

TILLINGTON · C4
Bell Inn
HR4 8LE On Hereford-Weobley road, NW of village OS 465454
☎ (01432) 760395
www.thebellinnuk.com
11-3, 6-11; 11-11 Sat; 12-6, 7-10.30 Sun
Draught Bass; Fullers London Pride; Wye Valley Bitter; guest beer

A popular, food-orientated pub, that particularly attracts families. The basic public bar (with pool table) acts as a focal point for the village, and contrasts with a plush, divided lounge and separate restaurant. The guest beer is from a local or regional brewery. The home-prepared food includes bar snacks (lunchtimes only), and main meals with daily specials and vegetarian options. No food Sun evenings - booking is recommended at most times. Bottled Tillington Hills Cider is sold by the glass. Full disabled facilities.

🏨 Q 🐕 ◖◗ 🍴 🍺 ♿ ✚ P

TITLEY · B3
Stagg Inn & Restaurant
HR5 3RL On B4355, in village
☎ (01544) 230221
www.thestagg.co.uk
12-3, 6.30-11 (not Mon); 12-3Sun
Hobsons Bitter, Town Crier; guest beer

Originally called the Balance Inn, as wool would have been weighed here, the inn was renamed and refaced in 1833, by the diarist Eliza Greenly. Thanks to her, we have the large light rooms in use today at the front of this splendid inn. This is unashamedly a gastro-pub, with nationally-renowned food being prepared from ingredients carefully sourced from small independent food producers. Outside the dining rooms, diners may elect to join local drinkers, in the cosy beamed bar - or even eat al fresco in the garden in summer. Very popular - booking for food is essential. Guest beers from local breweries; bottled local cider.

Q 🐕 🛏 ◖◗ P

TRUMPET · F5
The Verzon
Hereford Road, HR8 2PZ On A438, E of A4172 junction
☎ (01531) 670381
www.theverzon.co.uk
11-11 daily
Wye Valley Bitter; Butty Bach

Imposing and attractive red brick hotel set in large grounds with fine views towards the Malvern Hills. There are two main rooms served from a central bar. The atmosphere is friendly and convivial - with drinkers welcome, as well as diners with whom the home-prepared food is very popular. Light lunches and full à la carte meals are served. Full disabled facilities.

🏨 Q 🐕 🛏 ◖◗ ♿ 🍺 ✚ P ✂

Trumpet
HR8 2RA On A438, at A4172 junction
☎ (01531) 670277
11.30-2.30, 6-11; 12-3, 6-10.30 Sun
Wadworth 6X; Woods Shropshire Lad; guest beer, Westons Cider (summer only)

A black and white pub, dating from c.1456, partially opened out and refurbished to give a large single bar and two separate dining areas. Situated on a busy crossroads, it offers caravan and camping facilities. The wholesome menu uses fresh vegetables throughout - some from the pub's own garden (food not served Sun eves in winter). Hereford-Ledbury bus service 476 stops outside.

🏨 🐕 ◖◗ ⛺ 🍺 🍴 P ✂

ULLINGSWICK · E4
Three Crowns Inn
HR1 3JQ 1 mile E of village OS 605497
☎ (01432) 820279
www.threecrownsinn.com
12-3, 7-11; 12-3, 7-10.30 Sun
Hobsons Best Bitter; guest beer

An old, isolated pub that was once a cider house, with a newly built restaurant in bare brick and with modern flagstone floor. This has freed up space for a public bar to welcome drinkers. Alternatively, enjoy the award-winning cuisine, usually prepared with locally-sourced and organic ingredients, served in a delightfully bucolic atmosphere with candle-lit tables. Booking for food is advised. The guest beer is from the Wye Valley range. Facilities include a full disabled toilet and baby-changing facilities.

🏚 Q ⊛⊨ ◑ ⬓ ⴲ ♣ P ⚡

UPPER SAPEY — F2

Baiting House

WR6 6XT On B4203, in village
☎ (01886) 853201
12-3 (not Mon, Tue); 5-11 daily
Batham Best Bitter; Woods Shropshire Lad; guest beer: Westons Scrumpy cider

A multi-roomed pub characterised with a comfortable public bar, small lounge, conservatory, games room and restaurant. It has been unobtrusively extended to include an accommodation block. The name derives from the archaic meaning of bait - feed for horses and people on a journey. The regular Bathams is rare for the county. Traditional home-made lunchtime snacks and evening meals are prepared with locally-sourced materials wherever possible. Close to Upper Sapey Golf Club.

🏚 Q ⌂ ⊛⊨ ◑ ⬓ ♣ ⬣ P ⚡

UPTON BISHOP — F7

Moody Cow

Crow Hill, HR9 7TT At B4221/B4224 junction
☎ (01989) 780470
www.themoodycow.co.uk
12-2.30, 6.30-11 (closed Mon); 12-3 Sun
Hook Norton Hooky Bitter; Wye Valley Bitter; Golden Ale

An attractive stone-built pub with much exposed stonework inside. The emphasis is very much on food, but the drinker is also well catered for. The main bar is complemented by a dining room, a snug and the main restaurant - the latter which is in a converted barn. An extensive range of freshly-prepared food is offered, from a sandwich menu at lunchtimes through to full à la carte.

🏚 Q ⊛ ◑ ⬓ ⬧ ⊞ P ⚡

WALFORD — E8

Mill Race

HR9 5QS On B4234
☎ (01989) 562891
www.millrace.info
11-3, 5-11; 11-11 Fri,Sat; 12-11 Sun
Wye Valley Bitter, Butty Bach

A well-maintained exterior of white-painted rendered walls disguises the 17th century origin of this building, which is now once again called the Mill Race. The open-plan bar has two dining areas, and a further upstairs restaurant, all decorated and furnished in modern style. Local ingredients are used to prepare traditional English fare with a continental touch. Outside is an attractive garden, and there are full disabled toilet facilities.

🏚 ⊛ ◑ ⬓ ⊞ P ⚡

WALTERSTONE — B7

Carpenters Arms

HR2 0DX OS 340251
☎ (01873) 890353
12-11; 12-10.30 Sun
Breconshire Golden Valley; Wadworth 6X [G]

Known locally as the 'Gluepot' this lovely, unspoiled old pub, situated by the church in a scattered hamlet, is a favourite of ramblers. The front garden looks out to the Skirrid Mountain over the border in Wales. The ales are served direct from the cask, not on view from the tiny bar. Warmed by a fire in a superb old range, the two small drinking areas contrast with a restaurant to the rear. Good value home-cooked food is served, including Sunday evening. If the pub appears to be closed, try knocking the door!

🏚 Q ⊛ ◑ ⬓ P

WELLINGTON — D4

Wellington Inn

HR4 8AT ½ mile W of A49
☎ (01432) 830367
12-3 (not Mon), 6-11; 12-3, 7-10.30 Sun
Hobsons Best Bitter; Wye Valley Butty Bach; guest beers (2): Westons First Quality cider

Thriving traditional village hostelry with a welcoming public bar, where wooden benches contrast with opulent leather sofas. A separate barn-style restaurant is popular with diners. Winner of the Tastes of Herefordshire 2005, food is a real speciality, with bar snacks, an elaborate lunchtime and evening menu, and carvery on Sunday. The bar has interesting local photographs, board games and newspapers. Guest beers are mainly from micro breweries. Hereford-Leominster bus service 492 stops outside.

🏠 ❄ ◖◗ 🛏 ♣ 🐾 P

WELLINGTON HEATH — G5

Farmers Arms

Horse Road, HR8 1LS In village, east of B4214

☎ (01531) 632010

12-11(midnight Fri); 12-11 Sat,Sun,

Beer range varies (4)

A pleasant, secluded country pub, geared primarily to food, with a single open plan bar, refurbished in modern rustic style. Of the two separate dining areas, one opens on to a terrace and is for families and lunches, and the other for evening dining. Both offer freshly prepared modern cuisine. Live music alternate Thursdays. The beers are drawn from regional and local breweries.

🏠 ❄ ◖◗ ♣ P ✂

WEOBLEY — C4

Red Lion Hotel

Bell Square, HR4 8SE

☎ (01544) 318220

Reopened as a pub/restaurant in 2005, after a spell as a private hotel, but closed again. Was an outlet for local real ale.

Salutation

Market Pitch, HR4 8SJ

☎ (01544) 318216

www.thesalutationinn.co.uk

11-11; 12-10.30 Sun

Goffs Jouster; Spinning Dog HLA; Wye Valley Butty Bach

Dating back over 500 years The 'Sal', as it is known locally, combines an old ale and cider house with the adjoining black and white cottage. It now comprises a small public bar and a comfortable lounge bar and restaurant with

original timbers, an inglenook fireplace and barrel seats, plus an outdoor covered courtyard. Award winning traditional English style food is served and there is an excellent wine cellar. Booking is recommended for meals.

🏠 Q ❄ 🛏 ◖◗ 🛏 & 🚐 P ✂

Unicorn

High Street, HR4 8SL

☎ (01544) 318218

No real ale or cider

A timber framed inn dating back to the 17th century.

WESTON-UNDER-PENYARD — F7

Weston Cross

HR9 7NU On A40

☎ (01989) 562759

11.30-3, 6.30-11; 11-11 Sat; 12-10Sun

Draught Bass; Hancocks HB

An attractive creeper-clad stone building, on the edge of the village. The lounge bar, used mainly for dining, has an intimate feel while there is plenty of room in the public bar, with a pool table to one end. The wide-ranging menu (not served Sun eves) features home-cooked dishes and a particularly good selection of fish. Well behaved children are welcome and there is a large beer garden outside, with children's facilities.

❄ ◖◗ 🛏 & ⛺ 🚐 ♣ P

WHITBOURNE — G3

Live & Let Live

WR6 5SP In village, north of A44 OS 719566

☎ (01886) 821016

12-3(not Mon), 5-11; 11-11 Sat; 12-10.30 Sun

Hobsons Best Bitter; Wye Valley Bitter; guest beer: Thatchers Heritage Cider [G]

An attractive sixteenth century two-bar village pub with exposed beams and attractive bar furniture, not to be confused with its namesake on nearby Bringsty Common. The large public bar has a separate area with settees, and there is a small lounge adjoining the restaurant. Popular with locals who have two crib teams, darts and football teams. Traditional home-prepared English food is served, with fish a speciality. Live music last Friday of month.

🏠 🛏 ❄ ◖◗ 🛏 🚐 ♣ 🐾 P ✂

Wheatsheaf

Bromyard Road, WR6 5SF On A44
☎ (01886) 821319

No real ale or cider

An open plan roadside pub with a games room in the basement and extensive gardens to the rear.

Crown Hotel

HR9 7DB Just N of A40
☎ (01600) 890234
12-3 (not Mon, Tue), 6-11; 12-11 Sat, Sun

Draught Bass; Greene King IPA: Broome Farm Cider (summer)

A large, one-time coaching inn standing on the old main road. The main entrance leads to a lounge bar and a separate restaurant, which is airily furnished. To the rear is the excellent Tudor Bar, with bare stone walls, flagstone floor, skittle alley and pool table. The food ranges from bar snacks to full meals in modern pub style. The letting rooms are being refurbished.

🛏 ⛄ ❀ ◑ ▶ ⛁ 🚌 ♣ ☕ P

Boat

HR3 6EH Just S of A438
☎ (01497) 831223
11-11; 12-10.30 Sun

Courage Best Bitter, Directors; guest beer (summer): Bulmers Traditional Cider (summer)

An imposing early 20th century building on the site of a much older pub near the one-time ferry crossing. It consists of a public bar which caters for canoeists and walkers, a lounge and two restaurants enjoying splendid views of the River Wye. Traditional pub food is cooked using locally sourced ingredients and bar and restaurant menus are available.

🛏 ⛄ ❀ ◑ ▶ ⛁ ♿ Δ ♣ ☕ P

Compasses Hotel

Ford Street, HR6 9UN In village, off A4110 towards Ludlow
☎ (01568) 770705
www.thecompasseswigmore.com
12-2.30, 6-11; 12-12.30 Sat; 12-midnight Sun

Hobsons Best Bitter; Greene King Abbot; guest beer

Welcoming multi-roomed pub at the centre of village life. The oak panelled main bar has newspapers to read, whilst the public bar has pool, darts and an optional TV. Good-value, home prepared and cooked food in the main bar and in the separate restaurant (no food Mon lunchtime). Darts and pool; are played and a function room is available for hire.

🛏 Q ⛄ 🛏 ◑ ▶ ⛁ ♣ P ✄

Olde Oak

HR6 9UJ In village, on A4110
☎ (01568) 770247
12-3, 6-11; 12-11 Sat; 12-3, 7-10.30 (12-10.30 summer) Sun

Wye Valley Butty Bach; Three Tuns Three 8; guest beer

Ye Olde Oak is a timber framed two-bar village pub with bare stone walls and beams featuring in the comfortable public bar. The lounge at the rear leads to a separate restaurant in the conservatory. Home-made bar and restaurant meals are served every day except Sunday evening. Children and dogs are welcome. The interesting regular beers are complemented by guest beers from local micros or regional brewers, with an accent on Welsh brewers.

🛏 Q ⛄ ❀ ◑ ▶ ⛁ ♿ ♣ P

White Lion

Wilton Lane, HR9 6AQ Just off B4260
☎ (01989) 562785
www.whitelionross.co.uk
12-11; 12-10.30 Sun

Fullers London Pride; Wye Valley Hereford Pale Ale; Hook Norton Old Hooky; guest beer (not winter)

An attractive pub in a riverside setting with views across the River Wye and towards the town of Ross opposite. The bar is open-plan with exposed beams and stonework and a large stone fireplace. The restaurant is in a room called the gaol, which was originally part of a prison house adjoining the pub. English cuisine, freshly prepared from local ingredients, is served here and in the bar. The attractive garden leads down to the river.

🛏 ✸ 🍴 ◖◗ ⚠ 🚐 ♣ P

Wilton Court Hotel

Wilton Lane, HR9 6AQ Just off B4260
☎ (01989) 562569
www.wiltoncourthotel.com
11.30-3, 6.30-11 (11-11 summer); 12-3, 7-11 Sun
Wye Valley Butty Bach

A riverside hotel built in the 16th century as a courthouse for the Lords of Wilton. The bar, once the courtroom, has a beamed ceiling with original oak panelling. There is a restaurant, with a comfortable seating area adjoining, offering imaginative English cooking using local ingredients. A large garden has a petanque piste and extends across the road to the banks of the River Wye.

🛏 Q 🐾 ✸ 🍴 ◖◗ 🚐 ♣ P ✗

Sun

HR3 6EA On A438, in village
☎ (01544) 327677

Currently closed, but likely to reopen soon. Previously served real ale and food.

Cross Keys

HR1 3NN On A465 in Withington Marsh
(01432) 820616
5-11; 12-11 Sat; 12-4.30, 7-10.30 Sun,
Greene King Abbot; Hancocks HB; Wye Valley Butty Bach; guest beer

This outstanding, traditional local, run by the same landlord for over 30 years, is a family pub where conversation rules; a CAMRA favourite for its atmosphere. A single bar divides into two drinking areas, each with original stone walls, woodwork, a real fire and basic bench seating.

A folk jam session is held on the last Thursday in the month. The pub is on the Hereford - Bromyard bus route (418/419/420); camping can be arranged nearby. No food except Saturdays, when filled rolls are available.

🛏 ✸ ⚠ 🚐 ♣ P

Butchers Arms

HR1 4RF E end of village OS 618358
☎ (01432) 860281
12-3, 6.30-11 (midnight Fri); 12-3, 6-midnight Sat; 12-3, 6.30-10.30 Sun (shorter hours in winter)
Shepherd Neame Spitfire; Hook Norton Hooky Best; Wye Valley Butty Bach; guest beers

Mind your head! Low beams feature in this 16th Century two-bar pub, formed in Victorian times by combining a butchers shop and a beer house, looking out to a stream and attractive gardens. Favoured by out-of-city diners, it achieves a good mix of customers, including drinkers. Home-prepared food is served in both bars, and in the separate dining room (not Sun eve in winter). Guest beers are from local breweries. Bus service 453 from Hereford stops outside. The car park is further down the lane.

🛏 ✸ 🍴 ◖◗ ⚒ ♿ 🚐 P ✗

Crown Inn

HR1 4QP In village OS 611357
☎ (01432) 860468
12-3, 6.30(7 in winter)-11 (midnight Sat); 12-3, 6.30(7 in winter)-11 Sun
Black Sheep Bitter; Greene King Old Speckled Hen; Wye Valley Bitter

Situated next to the church, the Crown has a large bar, adorned with brewery memorabilia, (where children are welcomed), complemented by a restaurant and a 'public bar' area in the conservatory by the front door. The food is all home-prepared, and the extensive menu includes a large choice of imaginative vegetarian dishes. Curries feature on Monday evenings, whilst there is a carvery on Sunday lunchtimes. Bus service 453 from Hereford stops outside.

✸ ◖◗ ⚒ ♿ 🚐 ♣ P ✗

Lion Inn

HR3 6QN On A480, SE of village

WORMELOW

☎ (01544) 318332
12-2, 6-11; 12-3, 6-11 Sat; 12-3, 7-10.30 Sun
Wye Valley Butty Bach; guest beer (not winter)

Much extended in the 1980's, this roadside inn is known locally as the Ferney. A large, but cosy, lounge is complemented by a separate restaurant which offers locally-sourced food - specialising in vegetarian, vegan and gluten free dishes. Other dietary needs can be accommodated - ring to check. The guest beer comes from regional or micro-breweries.

🛏 Q ➳ ✿ ◖◗ ᴴ ⇦ 🐿 P

WORMELOW   D6

Tump
HR2 8EJ On A466
☎ (01981) 540233
12-3, 7-11 daily
Beer range varies (2)

An old roadside pub with an interesting beamed interior, named after a long lost burial mound that used to lie opposite. A single bar serves a lounge with whitewashed stone walls, a public bar area with pool table, and an adjoining restaurant. Home-made food is served, with Cornish fish a speciality.

🛏 ✿ ◖◗ ⇦ ✚ P

YARPOLE   D2

Bell
Green Lane, HR6 0BD In village, on road leading NW towards B4362
☎ (01568) 780359
11.30-3.30, 5.30 (6.30 Sat)-11; 12-3.30, 7-10.30 Sun
Hook Norton Hooky Bitter; Taylor Landlord; Wye Valley HPA

The main part of this 450 year old pub has been much altered, but the old timber-framed cider mill that houses the restaurant is superb, with the press and mill still in place. In addition, there are public and lounge bars. Now operated by the owners of the Hibiscus Restaurant in Ludlow, the style of the food is similar to what may be found in that famous town. Light or full meals are offered. Live music last Thu in month.

🛏 ✿ ◖◗ ⊡ ♿ P

To keep up to date with changes to
Herefordshire pubs, go to

www.herefordcamra.org.uk

Herefordshire Breweries

Arrow

Arrow Brewery, c/o Wine Vaults, 37 High Street, Kington, Herefordshire, HR5 3B3

☎ (01544) 230685

Email: deanewright@yahoo.co.uk

Deane Wright, brewed at Bridge Street for a year, supplying the Queens Head and his own pub, the Wine Vaults. A change of policy at the brewery led him to build his own 5-barrel brewery at the rear of the Wine Vaults and he re-started brewing for Christmas 2005. No other pubs are supplied.

Arrow Bitter (OG 1042, ABV 4%)

Quiver (ABV 5%)

Bridge Street

Brewing has ceased and planning permission obtained for residential use of the ex-Dunn Plowman brewhouse, to the rear of the Queens Head.

Dunn Plowman

Dunn Plowman Brewery, Unit 1A Arrow Court Industrial Estate, Hergest Road, Kington, Herefordshire, HR5 3ER

☎ (01544) 231993; **FAX** (01544) 231985

Email: dunnplowman.brewery@talk21.com

Tours by arrangement

Steve and Gaye Dunn started brewing in 1987 at the Royal George at Lingen, and moved to the Black Horse in Leominster in May 1992. Paul Harris joined Steve in 1993, and the brewery moved to the rear of the Queens Head in Kington  (then renamed Solstice Brewery, because the decision was made on 21st December). It continued to supply the Black Horse. The partnership was short-lived (see Marches), and Steve continued to brew intermittently whilst also brewing at the Three Tuns in Bishops Castle. Reverting to the name Dunn Plowman, production gradually built up to the full capacity of the plant. Additional capacity was secured in 2002, by taking over the SP Sporting Ales

Brewery (a short-lived operation based at Stoke Prior), and moving its equipment to a new site at Hergest, near Kington - together with the equipment from the Queens Head. Some of the SP range was integrated into the Dunn Plowman portfolio, but subsequently discontinued.

Steve and Gaye now also run the Olde Tavern in Kington, where most of the beers are featured. The brewery also supplies several free-houses within a 50-mile radius. Bottle-conditioned beers: Old Jake Stout, Kyneton Ale (ABV 5%), Golden Haze Wheat Beer (ABV 5%), Crooked Furrow.

Brewhouse Bitter (OG 1037, ABV 3.8%)

Early Riser (OG 1039, ABV 4%)

Sting (OG-1040, ABV 4.2%)

Kingdom Bitter (OG 1043, ABV 4.5%)

Old Jake Stout (OG 1046, ABV 4.8%)

Shirehorse Ale (OG 1053, ABV 5.5%)

Railway Porter (OG 1056, ABV 5.7%)

Crooked Furrow (OG 1063, ABV 6.5%)

Marches

Marches Brewing Co, The Old Hop Kiln, Claston, Dormington, Hereford, HR1 4EA

☎(01584) 878999

Email: littlebeer@totalise.co.uk

Tours by arrangement

Following the break-up of the Solstice Brewery partnership, Paul Harris set up the Marches Brewery on an industrial estate in Leominster. A range of beers was produced, including the house beer for the nearby Black Horse, and the excellent Jenny Pipes Summer Ale. The beers were sold into the free trade over a wide area. Paul ceased brewing in 2000, in order to transfer the equipment to a new site at Dormington, in conjunction with a proposed cider heritage centre. After a delay, due to the Foot and Mouth epidemic, the brewery was installed in two converted hop kilns, but the heritage centre now looks unlikely to be completed.

Brewing restarted in 2004, mostly to supply Paul Harris's Little Beer Shoppe in Ludlow, although he does supply some 20 local outlets. Paul works closely with hop growers to develop traditional beer styles, and produces single-varietal beers using new varieties of hops. A new bottling line is now operational. Bottle conditioned beers: Ludlow Gold, St Lawrence Ale.

Forever Autumn (ABV 4.2%)

Ludlow Gold (ABV 4.3%)

Dormington Gold (OG 1044, ABV 4.5%)

St Lawrence Ale (ABV 4.5%)

Mayfields

Mayfields Brewery, Bishops Frome, Worcester, WR6 5AS

☎ (01531) 640015 FAX (01885) 490428

Email: themayfieldsbrewery@yahoo.co.uk

Tours by arrangement

James Lewis is a native of Bishops Frome, who learnt to brew at Teignworthy Brewery in Devon after leaving college. In 2005, he took over the site and some of the equipment of the former Frome Valley Brewery - located in an 18th-century hop kiln. He insists on using only Herefordshire hops, many of which are grown on the brewery farm. James also produces real cider and perry to complement the beer range. Around 25 outlets are supplied direct. Seasonal beer: Crusader (ABV 4.3%, St George's Day-Trafalgar Day).

Pioneer (ABV 3.9%)

Naughty Nell's (ABV 4.2%)

Conqueror (ABV 4.3%)

Shoes

Shoes Brewery, Three Horseshoes Inn, Norton Canon, Hereford, HR4 7BH

☎/FAX (01544) 318375

Tours by arrangement

Frank Goodwin had been a home brewer for many years when, in 1994, he started brewing on a commercial basis for his pub. The beers are generally brewed from malt extract, although Peploe's Tipple is a full mash brew. The beers are normally only available at the Three Horseshoes, where some may be stored in casks and dispensed under a blanket of mixed gas.

Each September, Canon Bitter and Norton Ale are brewed with green hops. Bottle conditioned beer: Canon Bitter, Norton Ale, Farriers Ale (ABV 15.1%).

Norton Ale (OG 1038, ABV 3.6%)

Canon Bitter (OG 1040, ABV 4.1%)

Peploe's Tipple (OG 1060, ABV 6%)

Farriers Ale (OG 1114, ABV 15%)

Spinning Dog

Spinning Dog Brewery, 88 St Owen Street, Hereford, HR1 2QD

☎ (01432) 274998; ☎/FAX (01432) 342125

Email: jfkenyon@aol.com

Website: www.spinningdogbrewery.co.uk

Tours by arrangement

Following the success of the Jolly Roger brewpub in Worcester, a similar operation was set up in Hereford in 1991. This involved refurbishing the Bricklayers Arms with a bar in the shape of a galleon, and installing a small brewing plant at the rear. A pub sign in the form of a mural of a pirate brought conflict with the local planning authority.

By 1994, the Jolly Roger company retreated to Worcester, the pub was sold to Wye Valley and the brewery was dismantled. The nautical theme was retained and the pub became the Victory.

In 1999, the Victory was bought by Jim Kenyon, brother of Paul Kenyon then of Flannery's Brewery in Aberystwyth. The following year the brewery was re-equipped and, in recognition of the frequent gyratory antics of Jim's dog, Cassie, was named the Spinning Dog Brewery. Sadly Cassie will spin no more, having died in May 2006.

In 2002, the brewing capacity was expanded to 10 barrels, by installing vessels from the by now closed Flannery's, and the brewery has since been further upgraded.

The brewery serves the Victory, and has steadily grown to now supply some 300 outlets, including Wetherspoons. In 2005, it commissioned its own bottling plant, capable of producing 80 cases a day, some of which is sold via the internet. Bottling is carried out for other breweries.

Some of Flannery's beers have been integrated into the Spinning Dog range. Seasonal beers: Mutleys Mongrel (ABV 3.9%), Harvest Moon (ABV 4.5%), Santa Paws (ABV 5.2%). Bottle conditioned beers: Hereford Organic Bitter, Organic Oatmeal Stout.

> Chase Your Tall (OG 1036, AW 3.6%
>
> Hereford Organic Bitter (ABV 3.9%)
>
> Herefordshire Owd Bull (A8V 3.9%)
>
> Hereford Cathedral Bitter (OG 1040, ABV 4%)
>
> Mutleys Dark (OG 1040, ABV 4%
>
> Herefordshire Light Ale (ABV 4%)
>
> Top Dog (OG 1042, ABV 4.2%)
>
> Organic Oatmeal Stout (OG 1044, ABV 4.4%)
>
> Celtic Gold (OG 1045, ABV 4.5%)
>
> Mutleys Revenge (OG 1048, A8V 4.8%
>
> Mutts Nuts (OG 1050, ABV 5%)

Wilds

Wild's Brewery Ltd, Unit 6 Whitehill Park, Weobley, Hereford, HR4 8QE

☎ (01544) 319333

Website: www.wildsbrewery.com

Tours by arrangement

Pete Wild brewed for several years in Slaithwaite, near Huddersfield, but ceased brewing in 1997. His brewery equipment moved to Herefordshire, to the short-lived Woodhampton Brewery, and Pete and Wendy Wild  arrived seven years later to set up again in Weobley. Wilds output is mainly distributed nationally via wholesalers, but may be found increasingly in Herefordshire pubs. Seasonal beer: Wild Summer (ABV 4.2%).

> One (OG 1041, ABV 4.1%)
>
> SX (OG 1042, ABV 4.2%)
>
> Blonde (OG 104 5, ABV 4. 5%)
>
> Night (OG 1045, ABV 4.5%)

Wye Valley

Wye Valley Brewery, Stoke Lacy, Bromyard, Herefordshire, HR7 4HG

☎(01885) 490505; FAX(01885) 490595

Email: enquiries@wyevalleybrewery.co.uk
Website: www.wyevalleybrewery.co.uk

Shop Mon-Fri 10am-4pm, Tours by arrangement

Having left Guinness, Peter Amor set up the Abbey Brewery in Retford, Notts, in 1983. In 1985, the Abbey Brewery was moved to the Nags Head at Canon Pyon, where it displaced  another small brewery. Renamed Wye Valley, it started to serve the local trade as well as the Nags Head. The following year, the brewery moved again, to the stable block at the rear of the Lamb Inn in Hereford, which was then renamed the Barrels. Brewing capacity was significantly uprated in 1992.

In 1990, the Dorothy Goodbody name was introduced for seasonal beers. The computer-generated image of Dorothy was supplemented by some risqué stories to promote the brand. Stout and Golden Ale have become year-round brews. Special brews are also produced commemorating local luminaries. These are notable for the high quality of the associated display material.

With direct distribution over a wide area, and nationally via wholesalers, output grew steadily, and by the end of the decade the brewery was operating at full capacity. In 2001, part of the redundant premises of Symonds Cider of Stoke Lacy (between Hereford and Bromyard) was acquired, and a virtually all-new brewery

---

Descriptions of these beers, and all of the other real ales on sale in Herefordshire, are given in the Good Beer Guide.

OG (Original Gravity) is a measure of the malt or other sugars in the mash before fermentation

ABV (Alcohol by volume) is the percentage alcohol in the finished beer.

was installed - coming on stream in Spring 2002. The plant now has a capacity to brew 80 barrels a day.

Today Wye Valley is no longer a micro-brewery, and is proudly Herefordshire's first ever member of the Independent Family Brewers of Britain (IFBB). The scale of production is such that it now rubs shoulders with the likes of Fullers and Adnams.

Two pubs are owned, with plans for more over the next few years. Some 900 outlets are supplied nationwide. Seasonal beers: DG Springtime Ale (ABV 4%, Feb-Apr), DG Summertime Ale (ABV 4.2%, May-Jul), DG Autumn Ale (ABV 4.4%, Aug-Oct), DG Winter Tipple (A8V 4.7%, Nov-Jan). Twelve monthly guest beers and occasional specials are also available. Bottle-conditioned beers: DG Golden Ale, Butty Bach, DG Wholesome Stout, Country Ale (ABV 6%).

Bitter (OG 1037, ABV 3.7%)

Hereford Pale Ale (OG 1040, ABV 4%)

Dorothy Goodbody's Golden Ale

Butty Bach (OG 1046, ABV 4.5%)

Dorothy Goodbody's Wholesome Stout (OG 1046, ABV 4.6%)

A PINT'S A PINT - OR IS IT?

The big multi-national brewers, and the pub-owning companies have long resisted Government attempts to legislate that pubs must serve a guaranteed full pint when a customer asks for one. Where else would you buy something, and only expect to receive 90% or 95%? As a rough guide, if you place your thumb nail against the liquid line of your pint glass, that equivalent volume constitutes about 5% of your pint - and is worth around £1million per day to the industry's shareholders.

Many bar staff will top up a short pint without being asked. If you are not happy with your pint, you should politely ask for your glass to be topped up - and this should be done with good grace. If a top-up is refused, or you find a pub persistently trying it on with short measure, you should report the pub to the local Trading Standards Office.

The Herefordshire Environmental Health & Trading Standards Service, PO Box 233, Bath Street, Hereford, HR1 2ZF (01432) 261761.

Herefordshire Cider Makers

Ashgrove Orchards
Ash Grove Farm, Marden, Hereford, HR1 3EY.
☎ (01568) 797867
Website: www.hawnt.co.uk/ciderproducts

Bottled still cider and bottle-fermented cider, plus draught ciders soon to be available in a few nearby pubs.

Bridge Hill Farm
No contact details available. Cider on sale at the Victory, Hereford

Brook Farm Cider
Brook Farm, Wigmore, Leominster, Herefordshire, HR6 9UJ
☎ (01568) 770562
Website: www.brookfarmcider.co.uk

Bottled (pasteurised) and draught cider and perry. Visitors welcome but no farm gate sales at present.
Off A4110 in village just north of garage OS 413689

Bulmers
The Cider Mills, Plough Lane, Hereford, HR4 0LE
☎ (01432) 352000
www.bulmer.com

The world's largest cider maker is now a division of Scottish Courage. No real cider is made but Bulmers Traditional is contract-made by Westons. Following the takeover, the worst fears of rationalisation of orcharding and cider making have not been realised.

Butford Organics
Butford Farm, Bowley Lane, Bodenham, Hereford, HR1 3LG
☎ (01568) 797195
www.butfordorganics.co.uk

Bottled (inc Normandy style) and draught organic cider and perry. Fri - Sun & Bank Holidays 10 am - 5 pm
1½ miles N of A417 at Bodenham OS 543537

Cider Museum & King Offa Distillery
1 Ryelands Street, Hereford, HR4 0LW
☎ (01432) 354207
Website: www.cidermuseum.co.uk

Cider liqueur and brandy. January - March: 11am-3pm; April - October: 10am-5pm; November - March: Noon-4pm. Closed Sundays and Mondays excluding bank holidays & cider making festival weekend. Last admission to Museum one hour before closing – charges apply.

Dragon Cider
Dragon House, Putley, Ledbury, Herefordshire, HR8 2RG
☎ (01531) 670071

Cider orchards, open days, talks etc. Contract-made bottled cider. Visits by appointment only.

Dunkerton's Cider Co
Luntley, Pembridge, Leominster, Herefordshire, HR6 9ED
☎ (01544) 388653
Website: www.dunkertons.co.uk

Draught and bottled organic cider and perry. Visitors welcome. Shop open: Monday to Saturday all year, 10am - 6pm (except Xmas & New Year)
1 mile S of A44 at New Inn, Pembridge OS 395565

Great Oak Cider and Apple Co
Roughmoor, Eardisley, Hereford, HR3 6PR
☎ (01544) 327400

Wholesale only. Not available as own brand.

Gregg's Pit Cider & Perry
Gregg's Pit, Much Marcle, Ledbury, Herefordshire, HR8 2NL
☎ (01531) 660687
Website: www.greggs-pit.co.uk

Draught cider and perry. Visits and farm gate by appointment only.
S of B4024, ¾ miles SE of A449 junction OS 662323

Gwatkin Cider Co Ltd
Moorhampton Farm, Abbey Dore, Hereford, HR2 0AL
☎ (01981) 550258

Draught and bottled cider and perry. Farm shop 10am - 6pm daily.

On B4347, 2½ miles N of village

Henney's Cider Company Ltd
2 Tanhouse Court, Much Cowarne, Bromyard, Herefordshire, HR7 4JE

☎ (01885) 490800

Website: www.henneys.co.uk

No direct sales

Knights Cider Co Ltd
Crumpton Oaks Farm, Storridge, Malvern, Worcestershire, WR13 5HP

☎ (01684) 568887

Website: www.knightscider.co.uk

Bottled (pasteurised) and draught cider. Shop open Saturdays and Sundays all year, 10.30am - 5pm

On B4219, just N of A4103.

Ledbury Cider & Perry Co
Old Kennels Farm, Bromyard Road, Ledbury, Herefordshire, HR8 1LG

☎ (01531) 635024

Website: www.ledburycider.co.uk

Bottled cider. Farm gate sales any time

On B4214 N of Ledbury station

Lyne Down Cider & Perry
Lyne Down Farm, Much Marcle, Ledbury, Herefordshire, HR8 2NT

☎ (01531) 660543; mobile 07756 108501

Website: www.lynedowncider.co.uk

Draught and bottled cider and perry. All Year, daily, 9am - 6 pm (subject to availability — phone to confirm)

¼ mile W of A449, 1½ miles S of Much Marcle OS 646312

Mackay's Aylton Perry & Cider
Glebe Farm, Aylton, Ledbury, Herefordshire, HR8 2RQ

☎ (01531) 670121

Jus Apple Juice

Malvern Magic
Lower House Farm, Swinmore, Trumpet, Ledbury, Herefordshire, HR8 2SJ

☎ 07771 904127

Draught cider and perry. Visitors welcome but no direct sales. At present. Bottled products are expected to be available soon.

¾ miles N of A438, E of A417 junction (signed Munsley)

Newton Court Cidery
Newton Court, Leominster, Herefordshire, HR6 0PF

☎ (01568) 611721

Draught and bottled cider and perry including naturally sparkling/bottle fermented. Shop open all year, daily 8am - 6 pm (Sundays 10 am - 1 pm)

¼ mile W of B4361 just N of junction with A49 at Marlbrook. OS 508540

Oliver's Cider & Perry
The Old Hop Kilns, Moorhouse Farm, Ocle Pychard, Hereford, HR1 3QZ

☎/FAX (01432) 820569; mobile: 07768 732026

Website: www.theolivers.org.uk

Bottled and draught perries and ciders: Shop open Saturdays 10.0am to 4.0pm Easter to August Bank Holiday: (hours Sept - Jan tbc.)

Just off A417/A465 junction at Burley Gate, towards Gloucester OS 594468

Orgasmic Cider
Great Parton, Eardisley, Hereford, HR3 6NX

☎ (01544) 327244

Bottled cider. No direct sales.

Prospect Farm Cider Company Ltd
Upper Dormington, Hereford, HR1 4ED

☎ (01432) 851734

¼ mile S of A417 opposite Claston Farm

Rathays Old Goat Cider
Rathays, Sutton St. Nicholas, Hereford, HR1 3AY

☎ (01432) 880936

Wholesale only. Draught & bottled, blend and single variety, all dry.

Ross-on-Wye Cider & Perry Co
Broome Farm, Peterstow, Ross-on-Wye, Herefordshire, HR9 6QG
☎ (01989) 769556

Website: www.broomefarmhouse.co.uk

Normally known as Broome Farm Cider. Draught and bottled cider and perry. Visitors welcome to cider cellar 10am-6pm most days (ring to confirm, especially in winter)
¾ miles NE of A49 at NW end of village   OS 569250

Sarah's Cider
Temple Court, Bosbury, Ledbury, Hereford-shire, HR8 1HA
☎   07813 796053

Website: www.sarahscider.co.uk

Draught Cider. Tours available by arrange-ment.

H Weston and Sons Ltd
The Bounds, Much Marcle, Ledbury, Here-fordshire, HR8 2NQ
☎ (01531) 660233

Website: www.westons-cider.co.uk

Shop: Monday to Friday 9.00am - 4.30pm,
  Saturday and Sunday 10.00am - 4.00pm
  (Bank Holidays my differ)

Guided Tours: 11.00am and 2.30 pm 7 days a
  week. Adults £4.00 Children £2.50

Henry Weston Garden & Museum – free
  9am – 4.30pm daily

Shire horse dray rides Adult £2.50, Children
  £1.50, (approximately 40 minutes)
½ mile W of A449/B4024 junction

Bus Services to Rural Pubs in Herefordshire

Abbey Dore	440*	Kerne Bridge	34/35*	St Owen's Cross	38***		
Allensmore	X3/X4*	Kingsland	493/494/496*	Staplow	417*		
Almeley	462*	Kingstone	39* 449***	Staunton-on-Wye	446*		
Ashperton	672*	Kington	461/462*** 495/496*	Stoke Lacy	419/420*		
Bartestree	476***	Lea	33*	Stoke Prior	426*		
Bishops Frome	672/673*	Leintwardine	738/740*	Storridge	417*		
Bodenham	426*	Letton	446*	Stretton Sugwas	461/462***		
Bosbury	417*	Little Dewchurch	37*	Sutton St Nicholas	426*		
Bridge Sollers	446*	Lugwardine	476***	Swainshill	446*		
British Camp	675* Fri-Sat***	Luston	492***	Tarrington	476**		
Bush Bank	501*	Lyonshall	461/462*** 495/496*	Tillington	437/477*		
Canon Pyon	501*	Madley	449***	Titley	468*		
Clehonger	39* 449***	Marden	426*	Travellers Rest	32***		
Colwall	675* Fri-Sat***	Mordiford	453*	Trumpet	476*** 672*		
Dilwyn	507*	Mortimers Cross	494*	Upton Bishop	32***		
Dorstone	39*	Moreton-on-Lugg	492*	Walford	34/35*		
Eardisland	496*	Much Birch	38***	Wellington	492*		
Eardisley	446* 462**	Much Dewchurch	412*	Weobley	461/462***		
Ewyas Harold	440*	Munstone	426*	Weston-u-Penyard	33*		
Fownhope	453/454*	Newtown	672*	Whitbourne	420*		
Garway	412*	Norton Canon	461/462***	Whitchurch	34*		
Goodrich	34*	Orleton	492***	Wilton	37* 38***		
Gorsley	32***	Pembridge	496*	Withington	418/420*		
Grafton	38***	Peterchurch	39*	Woolhope	453*		
Hampton Bishop	453*	Peterstow	38***	Woonton	461/462*		
Harewood End	38***	Richards Castle	492***	Wormelow	412/416*		
Hoarwithy	37*	Shobdon	493/494/496*				

Services shown offer at least one opportunity for a return journey
NB information does not apply to Sundays

Key: * minimal service, daytime only
  ** minimal service, daytime and evening
  *** moderately frequent all day

WANT TO KEEP IN THE BEER PICTURE?

It's all on the internet.....

Go on-line at **www.herefordcamra.org.uk** for all the up-to-date information on pubs, beers and what's happening in CAMRA across the county of Herefordshire. On the Herefordshire CAMRA website you will find:

- Alterations to the pub details in this guide - keep your guide bang up to date
- Details about local BEER FESTIVALS - not just *Beer on the Wye*, but other CAMRA and pub beer festival across the county, and further afield.
- Stories covering important CAMRA campaigns affecting local brewers, pubs and cider-makers.
- What's On: details of Herefordshire CAMRA activities and trips - we visit breweries, cider-makers, pub tours and much more.
- What's happening on the local pub scene - including what pubs are selling what beers and ciders - you'll read it all here first from the people on the ground

Remember www.herefordcamra.org.uk for all you need to know.

.........or at your local pub

Herefordshire CAMRA also publishes five-times-a-year a free newsletter, *Hereford Hopvine*. This is distributed to around 80-100 pubs across the county. News, both local and national, views and pictures, all in a light-hearted style make this an interesting read. It also details what's happening in Herefordshire CAMRA and on the local pub scene, with adverts for beer festivals, pubs and other beer-related activities. Look out for it in your local pub!

If the Hopvine doesn't find its way to your local, get in touch with us, and we'll do our best to get it there.

Publicans....

Get your message direct to your target market - advertise in the *Hopvine*. At least 1500 copies of each issue are distributed to up to 100 pubs within the county and many further afield, plus beer festivals around the region. Prices start from as little as £26, and there are attractive discounts for ads in consecutive issues. If you're not a design expert, you can send your ideas to us, and we'll do the rest. Contact Paul Grenfell on (01432 851011) or paulgrenfell@aol.com

GOOD BEER GUIDE:

YOUR GATEWAY TO A WORLD OF BETTER PUBS & BETTER BEER!

First published in 1972, and published every year since, the best-selling CAMRA *Good Beer Guide* is the definitive book for finding good pubs that sell good beer and cider. Listing over 4300 pubs across the length and breadth of the UK - this should be

your first port of call when planning a trip out to a pub in an unfamiliar area: you can be absolutely reassured when referring to the guide, as the pubs have been exclusively selected by CAMRA volunteer members. No payment is taken for any entry, unlike in some other so-called 'guides'. Let the father of all the guides show you the way - the *Good Beer Guide* lists pubs for families, country pubs, town pubs, new pubs, good food pubs - and every-thing in between. It's got the lot. It'll also tell you what we think are the top 26 pubs for Herefordshire - wouldn't you just like to know?!

Priced at £13.99, the book is fully illustrated, and has a number of challenging and interesting articles to read. Pub descriptions are detailed, but easy to read. County-by-county maps make for ease of reference.

Besides the Good Beer Guide, CAMRA also publishes many other books - covering a wide range of subjects, including: home-brewing, Belgian Beers, Cider, Pub Food, pub accommodation, pub walks - and even produces Pub Guides to the Continent. A number of these books are covered on pages 87/88, and the full list of CAMRA publications can viewed (and purchased) by going on-line at **www.camra.org.uk**

PUB REPORT FORM - PLEASE LET US HAVE *YOUR* VIEWS:

We need your feedback and views. Has anything changed at a pub in this book? Dis-agree with anything we've said? Something new happening, or a change to the beer range or quality, hours, food etc? Please let us know using this form, or just write to us at Herefordshire Pubs, 3 Goodwood Walk, HEREFORD. HR4 9NN. Alternatively, please use the on-line form at www.herefordcamra.org.uk

Your Name _____

Address _____

_____

Name of Pub_____ Town/Village_____

Comments

What is CAMRA all about ?

CAMPAIGN FOR REAL ALE

Enjoy your beer? Like decent pubs? Fed up with being taken for granted at your local? Annoyed about a pub refit or closure? Concerned about the future of your village pub? Or do you just fancy a trip to a brewery or country pub with other like-minded people? If the answer is yes to any, or all of these questions, then it's probably time you joined us. Can over 80,000 (and growing) CAMRA members really be wrong? CAMRA champions the cause of the pub-user and the real beer drinker. Now is the time to add your voice. With nearly 200 branches nationwide, and around 180 CAMRA beer festivals, you'll be joining an active and effective organisation. CAMRA membership can be both rewarding and fun.

Add YOUR VOICE TODAY - CAMRA campaigns on issues as diverse as beer quality in pubs, taxation, brewery takeovers and pub closures. Being a CAMRA member has many benefits:

- You receive a monthly quality newspaper, *What's Brewing*, which besides listing beer festivals, brewery trips and branch social activities, brings you lively and informed stories about ongoing CAMRA campaigns, breweries, beer, cider and pubs from across the country.

- You will be entitled to free (or discounted) entry to the many CAMRA Beer festivals around the UK. Locally, there are beer festivals each year in Hereford, Worcester, Bromsgrove, Redditch, Tewkesbury, Cardiff and Shrewsbury. You can even volunteer to help organise, or work at, a beer festival!

- Members are entitled to generous discounts on a whole host of interesting and professional CAMRA publications and beer-related merchandise. This includes a big discount on the annual best-selling Good Beer Guide, that lists the best 4,500 pubs in Britain for real beer and cider.

- You will be a part of an active consumer movement, and there will be a local branch near you. Local branches campaign on issues and have a strong events programme. This is your opportunity to join other like-minded people doing what they enjoy - visiting the pub!!

Herefordshire CAMRA is the local branch. So what do we do? We publish this Pub Guide for a start! We also organise an annual beer festival in Hereford - *Beer on the Wye*. We have a website at www.herefordshirecamra.org.uk, and we publish a five-times-a year free newsletter - *Hereford Hopvine*. We have a good track record on campaigning - especially in the area of rural pubs: Herefordshire CAMRA has lead the way in preventing the unnecessary closure of many pubs across the county. We also ENJOY what we do: we organise regular events including visits out by minibus to country pubs near and far, plus breweries and other attractions. Why not get involved? - you never know, you might end up surveying pubs for this guide, or even helping to organise *Beer on the Wye* next year! Everyone is welcome. By being a member you can make a difference. Please don't leave it to others to fight for YOUR local or YOUR favourite beer - the big brewers and pub companies would love you to do that, and tomorrow might be too late!

JOIN CAMRA TODAY - *VALUE YOUR MEMBERSHIP, ENJOY YOUR MEMBERSHIP.*

£12.99
(members £10.99)

£9.99
(members £7.99)

£7.99
(members £5.99)

Do you feel passionately about your pint? Then why not join CAMRA?

Just fill in the application form (or a photocopy of it) and the Direct Debit form on the next page to receive three months' membership FREE!

If you wish to join, but do not want to pay by Direct Debit, please fill in the application form below and send a cheque, payable to CAMRA to: CAMRA, 230 Hatfield Road, St Albans, Hertfordshire, ALI 4LW.

Please check www.camra.org.uk or phone 01727 867201 for current membership prices   [ref Herefordshire Pubs]

☐ Single Membership (UK & EU) £ _____

☐ For under-26 Membership £ _____

☐ For 60 and over membership £ _____

For partners' joint membership add £ _____ (for concessionary rates both members must be eligible for the membership rate). Life membership information is available on request. If you join by Direct Debit you will receive three months' membership extra, free!

Title _____ Surname_____

Forename(s)_____

Address_____

_____

Postcode_____Date of Birth_____

Email address_____

Signature_____

Partner's details if required

Title_____ Surname_____

Forename(s)_____

Date of Birth_____

Email address_____

☐ Please tick here if you would like to receive occasional emails from CAMRA (at no point will your details be released to a third party).

Page 88